Allison,

We're looking forward to meeting you! I hope you'll enjoy and find meaning from this book.

Nada said the book has been with him for most of his life.
Blessings, Glen

FACE-OF-THE-RISING-SUN

Nada

Library of Congress Control Number: 2019939318

ISBN: 978-1-940025-44-5.

Printed in the United States of America

10 9 8 7 6 5 4 3 2 1

1. Native American---Stories 2. Initiation---vision quests 3. Transcendental philosophy---metaphysics I. Title.

PRAISE FOR NADA AND "FACE-OF-THE-RISING-SUN"

The former "Men's Movement" was accompanied by both jokes about gushy, effeminate, drumming men and by legitimate concerns about appropriating Native American beliefs and practices. While such concern was valid, I think reconnection was a larger impetus for the men participating. At some time in the genetic past, most cultures met around the village tree or fire and sang, danced, chanted, and drummed, as a means of passing on the rituals, stories, beliefs, healing methods and other foundational practices which held them together. We, in 21st Century America, have lost too much of that.

Face-of-the-Rising-Sun offers readers a corrective to that separation. Nada takes us on a deep, informative, and more importantly, formative journey into a world where Nature is the means by which "God" self-reveals, grabbing the initiate and introducing him/her to the inner lives of Air, Water, and the Animal, Vegetable and Mineral manifestations of Nature which are of most importance to persons living in proximity to those elements in that place. "God" is in the details and the details are in a physical, natural world which is totally capable of communication with the true seeker. Are you that seeker, and are you willing to let go of conceptual, dogmatic belief and experience another way of interacting with Life, with Nature....with The Divine?

—Jeri Lynn Miller, PhD (Mythological Studies),
friend and colleague of Nada

I believe I was led to Nada. Or Nada to me. The greatest honor of my time as a chaplain in hospice was to visit Nada every Monday of his final seven months in his body. Conversation was sometimes difficult but very quickly I was aware I was sitting in front of someone who has "medicine." We would talk some and he would joke with a twinkle in his eye, but the most significant thing I could do for Nada was to read him the words from THIS book one last time. In some mystical way through my voice combined with his words found here, he drank of his own medicine. His own words from this book describe the beauty of our seven month of Monday visits.

"As I share my journey with you," he would say, "I look into your eyes to find where I have been and who I am." His tears flowed. His heart full.

And me? Forever...changed...

—Rev. Paul Barber, Chaplain,
Kindred Hospice, Liberty Lake, Washington

ALSO BY NADA

Mary Magdalene, A Mystical Journey
Vol 1 – Mary's Gospel
Published by Spirit Press, Portland, Oregon (2007)

DEDICATED TO

Glen Scott.
Nada would say he wanted to be where you were.
You blessed him with love, care and devotion and,
Nada openly and fully acknowledged, appreciated and loved you too.

The Lhaq'temish, the Lummi People,
and
Danita Washington,
Friend and mentor, who lives on the Lummi Reservation near
Bellingham, Washington.

FACE-OF-THE-RISING-SUN

Is proudly sponsored by **One More Time, Inc.**

One More Time, Inc. is a North Idaho nonprofit, 501(c)3, established in 2017, with the mission to help adults with life-limiting conditions enjoy a memorable experience "One More Time." The goal is to tailor each experience to the individual's wish as much as possible.

After the sudden death of her beloved father, aged 58, One More Time's founder and CEO, Tiffinay Walker envisioned this inspiring idea. Although she can no longer have memorable moments with her father she finds it fills her heart to offer and create these "One More Time" experiences for others.

Tiffinay met the author, Nada, through a longtime friend, Lacie, who is a social worker. Lacie spoke of a patient she had that wanted help getting a book published. Although this was a novel request, Tiffinay researched local publishing companies, selecting Bitterroot Mountain Publishing House LLC whom she introduced to Nada.

One More Time, Inc. currently can provide experiences in the five Northern Counties of Idaho and Spokane, Washington.

The board at One More Time wishes to thank all contributors for their generous gifts and asks for continued donations from the community. They currently have several "One More Time" experiences in the planning phase and they hope never to have to say "no" to someone's last wish.

"One More Time" can be contacted via their Facebook page.

Contents

INTRODUCTORY NOTE

For the 1991 Winter Solstice, I took the pages of this manuscript to the Lummi Reservation smoke house fires. The Lummi are an active coastal Northwest tribe. All night the Star-Nation reviewed what is written here. They brought forth many issues: Some wondered if these words should be made, without knowing the ears and eyes which will gather them in. Others wanted to know by what claim I brought them to you. All night I was with our Ancestral Elders in the Longhouse. My heart was open before them for examination.

My life was offered as a gift.

I was not called to answer them, but to be changed by their confrontation.

I agreed to add or delete anything in the manuscript that they directed. These pages are, even now, under our Ancestors' watch-care. Each word carries the meaning they want it to have for you.

It was in deep gratitude and strict discipline that I took each page, and presented it in flames, to be received or rejected by Spirit. No page was missing – from Title and Introduction through to the end of the last story. Spirit rejected no page. Every page was eaten by the fire and digested by the sky. I emerged from the longhouse as the sun peeked over the horizon.

At that moment, three swans rose, and flew up and across the Face-of-the-Rising-Sun.

The meaning of these words is as it is for you, according to your relationship to the Spirit who lives and dwells in you. The words are more than a report about someone's life journey, or symbols of a spirit-quest. They hold life-power. Their medicine is yours.

Please note that this story represents moons when the tobacco in our peace pipe was sweet. It did not have a bite from our friendship with the white-man. This was when our traditions were not a reaction to outside cultures, but were an affirmation of ourselves. This was when thoughts were carried in images rather than concepts. This book is a serious attempt to use the heart-talk of our people, through the nature analogies of our old-think ways. I searched everywhere to find our talk-way again.

I am honored by being empty, like the air-sky in which shines the sun, moon and stars. The Spirit of Face-Of-The-Rising-Sun speaks to you from these pages. They are his medicine-quest and his story-words of wisdom. Since February 4, 1989, when these messages first started coming, I have been his breath, between life and death.

I am Nada

INTRODUCTION
MEDICINE POWER

I greet you in peace, my sacred family. To you I offer the pipe of friendship. I am Face-Of-The-Rising-Sun; bringer of medicine power. For the wisdom of my moons, I give thanks to Great-Spirit, who is the source of all things.

As I share my journey with you, I look into your eyes to find where I have been, and who I am.

You are my people.

I give thanks that my life has lived up to the hopes of my youth. I have worn many holes in my moccasins walking the life-trail. I can tell you that our Ancestors' pathway is reliable and lasts long. It is deep in the earth. I give thanks to Great-Star-Nation for the strength to tell you these stories. For them to be passed on through our children, is my deep gratitude. This task had to be done through me. I lift my voice to sky and earth. I show you my heart. May this sacred offering be received by the Spirit which walks between us and helps us share the power of All-Mystery.

My many moons have taught me that it is not 'sickness' that a person brings for healing. What people bring is spiritual need.

We are each the magic presence of the Mysterious-One. If anything blocks this, we will feel lost or become ill. We will have wounded life powers and may lose our trail footing. If we do not take these blocks away, and live our full mystery, our Spirit-waters dry-up, like a puddle in the sun.

We end and blow away, like dust-wind. Our bodies hold the trail-guide, which we must follow to reach our fulfillment.

If health goes wandering, we know that we have missed the pathway. Our bodies can be trusted to show us the way. Illness guides us to the power alive in us. It puts before our eyes that we must live Spirit's power. Illness disciplines us to do things the way Spirit lives and moves. Medicine brings us in touch with how to do this. It teaches us how to keep our Holy-Mystery alive.

To find a person's medicine, I had to learn what Spirit wanted them to bring into their sacred-power path. This Spirit-power was in all creatures, for we were Spirit's movement. We were made from our Ancestors' dust. Our bodies shadowed their Unseen-Mystery. We hunted for The-Unseen, and found It inside ourselves, through vision-songs and mystery-dances.

Everything had Spirit-Life, everything; the stones, the mountains, the lakes. Sometimes our ears stretch to hear them speak, but their message was always clear. When we waited in silence, they shared their wisdom-secrets. In silence, we learned what power filled the herbs and made the stars to shine with fire. We found what changed the night to day and made the seasons grow. From nature, we learned that everything is good, just as it is. It is as it is, and nothing more. All things were bound together by their good. That was health. It was what is natural. These were the power ties between us and All-Mother. They had to be honored. These powers brought healing and created our sacred ceremonial places.

We were always quiet about our medicine, and held the healing mysteries to ourselves. We did not talk about them; we lived them. Talking took away their benefits. It tied their sacredness into knots by words. We did not discuss our dreams or visions, our secrets or our ways. Words pushed the Holy-One away. In the life-walk itself, Power stood behind words and actions.

Those who took vows, to openly live the sacred earth-sky powers, received our medicine ways. It demanded strong discipline. It took many moons of hard work and full trust. Spirit always selected these people.

No person could choose to work with medicine power. No one could know what to choose, for our knowledge came from another place. When Spirit power came, it was so strong that the person had to act, or else die from it.

Our power came from Spirit. It told us what to do and how to be. We did not choose. What we would have done or said, would have been foolish-stupid. If Spirit did not do it, the actions would not accomplish anything. If medicine power is misused, there is big danger. It destroys the user.

THIS IS A SERIOUS WARNING.

All who imitate medicine power invite a strength which becomes part of them. If they are not ready for this power, bad things happen. The person can become unbalanced or be destroyed. Spirit orders all things and is not gentle, for it always has its way. It will not be played with, by anyone.

The great wonder of medicine power was that Spirit created every part of our lives. The Sacred brought everything to us that happened, and gave us the power for all change.

Even the smallest things had their place.

Medicine plants, as Spirit-life-powers, were gathered in a sacred manner and at special seasons. We gathered them only with permission from their Chief. Once this was granted, we waited for as many opportunities as we had fingers. Then we gathered only what was necessary. Before gathering them, we prayed in humble respect to the herbs. We also honored the directions and their place in our lives, as we chanted:

"We take you to your brothers and sisters, as good medicine. We take you to the ones who will know happy days of health and strength."

These plants became strong to mend any tear holes in a person's spirit blanket, of which body illness or emotional craziness were shadows. Spirit used these medicines, for every healing was a Spirit action. Mending the body or mind was the sign that Spirit brought health.

Besides medicine plants, Great-Sun-Mystery brought healing in mountains, animals, winds, birds, and fire. We received great power from these. They were our life-gifts, and each one had its own strength. These things followed their natural ways.

That order became my medicine path. All nature was alive and holy, so my way was to be one with its sacred flow.

I knew the quiet healing of the land. Its life was thick and rich. Its way was free and gentle. I learned land talk and heard the earth's many voices.

Earth was made for us all. It was good healing, and our peace was part of all it was. Earth provided her soil for our strength. When our skin touched her, we were close to great power. She was our soothing-comfort. The ground was alive. As we walked without moccasins, in the dust, we felt the strength of her free giving. We lay our wounds on her or put mud on them to draw healing power through.

We went for strength and care, to the Stones-Which-Cannot-Be-Moved. These are our Mother's records. Here her strong medicines made the mountain herbs powerful.

The earth soils guided us how to use them. Mud was used for any outside problems, such as bee or ant stings. It drew out the poison. Clay was used for inside problems. It was placed on the body to draw the inside and outside powers together, and to tie them, like a broken bow string. Colored clays were healing gifts. We rubbed them on a person's body, or blew them through wing bones, in sacred rituals. When we took these free gifts from the earth, we chanted:

"The earth is sacred. All upon it is holy. We are the earth. We share its healing medicine."

Other health giving powers were water, air, heat and cold. We poured water over ourselves, soaked in it, sweat it, and drank it through our bodies. We often mixed it with other medicines, for its thin, clear layer held the power to weave healing into any illness.

Fire spoke the power-flame so we mixed fire and water. We would listen to hear them singing together. To purify ourselves we would sweat. We dug a hole in the ground and covered it with cured willow sticks and a layer of animal skins, whose medicine blessed our purification. On the hot stones, we threw water and sage. The hot stone water released ancient lessons and entered our bodies with the heat. This put us in touch with earth and our Star-Nation Ancestors.

We called our sweat lodge, "Grandfather" because of its warm heart and easy acceptance. The stories and songs we shared there, taught us to bring our bodies close to nature's ways. They showed us our place in the happenings of life.

Many times, I used sky, by blowing soft air through a hollow eagle bone, onto the person's face. This spirit filled their surrounding body and had magical health powers. They usually felt it as a fire-wind. I would have them make a breath pattern. This let their life make an easy tie with Spirit. Together we filled our lungs. This made harmony patterns, which let full medicine power bring healing. I also used an eagle wing fan. Wing-beating air brought soft power and helped the person receive sky medicine.

The sky is alive. It carried the clouds and wind, the lightning and the rain. Sky-power let us walk long trails and safely meet any dangers. Sky-strength was our joy-blessing. All sound was the voice of Change-Chief-Of-Sky-Spirits. So, we learned to listen quickly. The voices that made our lives work we heard in the canyon echoes, the whisper of falling waters, the wrestling leaves and in bird songs.

Heat and cold, fire and ice, sunshine and darkness were all used to make our healing stick together. Along with water, air and earth, I also used warm charcoal, hot weed poultices and the inner heat of the person's body. Warmed shells, sucked the skin into hot swells. Sweating and rapid cooling were ways of making a basket pattern for weaving one's spirit and body together.

Our use of Sun was very important. Every day, as Star-Child brought up the sun, we greeted it with our arms stretched wide above our heads. We invited Dawn to spill over us, as a cleansing and protecting medicine. The act of spreading our hands to light-power, put us in agreement with Spirits all around us. When Sun fell upon Earth, with life and beauty, it brought us peace and joy. The calm presence of Spirit shone as light and heat. As Sun rose higher we would often chant:

"Great-Mystery, our Chief, arise! Sun-Chief is sacred and shines of the Unseen. Thank you. Thank you."

This action of honor and gratitude brought health-power into our hearts. It was our every day gift. Being well was provided through nature, but it endured through our hearts. If we did not pay attention to our heart medicine, it brought bad moods, unhappiness, arguments and change slowness. The only things which I found that settled these muddy waters, were the spiritual directions. We had to bring our bodies in line with the earth's pulling forces. This also brought fast healing for broken bones, hits on the head and injuries from falls. Have a person spin with, or against, the directions made emotional illness fly away. The spin-direction depended on whether they had to unwind or to wind up. To make our minds agree, I turned all directions with the person, while touching the Spirit-blanket around them.

The directions up and down were very important. Whether a person sat, stood up, or would lie down, made a difference in the healing. If they lost knowing who they were, I had them stand or sit facing the sun. If they could no longer hear their inside voice, lying down was good medicine.

Inside and outside medicines were used for different spiritual needs. Things put inside were for the Deep-Inside-Spirit. Things put on the outside were for one's Over-Spirit. Usually we used both inside and outside medicines.

Moon and Sun were strong powers. Inside things were treated in moon light. Things on the skin were treated during the darkness moon. Helping a person with high and low activity, the moon cycles were respected and used. If the importance of this was pushed aside, people could make up something that sounded good, but was a lost guide for me. Movement set up inside power. Areas with no movement lost their health.

Everything we did was sacred. It was our earth-life harmony. So, we didn't throw motions away. We made everything in agreement. Our dances showed this. The movement power of each animal, bird, tree, mountain, stream or sky became our medicine. Putting our movements together with nature was our way of putting ourselves together with its power. Along with rhythm, silence was our strongest medicine. It taught us how to live as Spirit would have us be. Silence is the wisdom, hiding behind words and thoughts, waiting to be found. Silence and rhythm united all. (Hy-ya-ho!)

When I was asked to decide about a person's illness, I hooted to call Spirit. I then did a dance-song. People helped by drumming and using rattles. These sounds brought us together for healing. Often, I used power objects from my medicine bag. When the throbbing life-force was in me, the person's illness became clear. My dance-song-trance let me know if my guiding Spirit wanted to help the ill person.

Together we saw where the sickness was on the person's body, so I could know how to bring Spirit harmony. Medicine-power plants helped. They did not bring healing; they provided renewal-spirits. Before taking power herbs, I cleansed and purified my hands in the sacred smell of burning sage. This way, I was guided in how to divide the herbs and work with their medicine power. This purification made Spirit very strong. The power of touching with holy hands, made everything go away which might keep medicine from working.

My presence made healing power around the person. This helped when their strength was low. It pulled us together. This shared power was like walking the trail with each other; we carried Spirit-strength in the same direction. This helped cure such illness as emptiness of spirit, darkness of mind, fear of heart, or pain of body.

Another thing I want to mention: Healing sometimes did not remove the person's problems right away. The spirit power, which had been moved aside, creating the person's problem, had to finish its cycle. How the person gave their life energy to a problem, made a difference in how fast their physical problems healed. Some people grabbed their sickness even if it made hurts for them.

I and the person seeking help, had to work together as one person. We gave up our physical bodies and stepped into heart-unity and sexual power. We felt Spirit in our birth scars.

This helped us mix together, as we breathed the same breath. Usually I closed my eyes and put my hand on the person's shoulder. This way I could see inside the person. We became one mind, one desire, one freedom, and one joy. Together we let go of everything which stopped life and health. We shared one vision, which brought us into step with nature. We explored the changes needed to keep health alive. Spirit tied our lives together.

If there were barriers between us these had to go. There could be no limits. Our aloneness had to drop. We became one-power, whose way was the healing path. This was made by touching, humming the person's name, and waiting for their vision to play on my mind. Without full oneness between us, only small healing could happen.

Dried tree sap resins from pine, fir, hemlock and cedar were burned when opening ourselves to one another.

Often the person drank cascara bark tea on the before sleep. This made their inside cleansing complete and let us hear the voices of our sky family with ease. Earth-Mother, Sister-Moon and Brother-Stars had to agree with the healing. I looked for council from each of these.

So, we sang the wordless songs we danced. Most chants were beyond words and often included actions; imitating animals or nature-powers. These medicine chants included: The antelope chant-dance for softness; the thunder chant for great and swift power; the bear song for earth-strength; the eagle dance-chant for sky-power; the owl songs when death seemed near; the buffalo chant for deep earth-power; the sounds of a bee for courage; the crane song for life-power; the beaver song for endurance; weasel-chant for action; and the otter for strong active movement.

We drummed or rubbed rawhide discs toward the ill person, so the drum's healing energy could be directed through them like a river canyon for the wind. I, friends or family would dance. With drums, rattles and chants, we rushed toward and then away from the person; in Big-Water's movements; inviting the Spirits. This held the medicine power around the person wanting to be healed. The medicine was strongest, when our voices sounded like the wind blowing across a rawhide string. The power of our voices mixed with the drum, to beat out the heart of the world.

Breeding energy was deep Spirit power, creating relaxed but strong wellness. Focusing this power onto only certain body parts brought lack of spiritual balance to the whole person. But to deny its power, drained people of life and made them not know where or who they were.

If spiritual balance was not held, a simple diet change was not enough to make physical health. To bring spiritual balance, we waited for the Spirit which spoke to us most clearly. This might be a Spirit of the lake, trail, stars, open horizon, prairie flowers, dawn – or many others. Listening only to that voice, we brought our lives into harmony with its decisions.

The strongest medicine Spirit was the person's spirit animal. Their song helped bring this power near. The oils of their sacred animal brought healing power close. All, together, we became spiritually alive. The basis of all these stories are from my half Shoshone father and the old Indian who lived in a log cabin in the ravine above our house, where I was growing up. We provided food for him and he provided stories for us. He was at the end of his life's journey.

In the pages of this book are stories and my thoughts about people and medicine. They are inspired by the Old Indian, the last member of the Northwest Umpqua tribe. They are told as I sit far moons away, for I have come to my ending. With these words, I give you my medicine bag, my life-power.

I am ready to meet the Old-Ones, who have followed me along the trail and now wait for me.

One day I shall rise again from the Big-Waters.

I have spoken.

PART 1

I

MOON SHIFTS ITS SHADOW

It was the Season-Of-The-Death-Wind,
when cleansing white crystals fell
down from the sky,
to renew our sleeping Earth-Mother.

Blizzard-Maker's strong medicine was always cold.
There was no hiding from its scratch-sting.

With its sacred arrival,
we painted our faces with clay,
mixed in deer fat,
and danced a wind-breath drum beat.

With quiet drums,
we chanted from our breath clouds:
    "Grandfather-Death,
    we give our bodies to you!
    Our journey is ended.
    Our life is complete."

NADA

It was a slow snake pulse;
a soft resonate beat,
which held against the drifting wind.

Until the storm died,
we quietly sang
around large smoke lodge fires
and danced without moccasins
in the earth dust of our Ancestors;
stopping only to take sexual partners.

This made bodies for the Creative-Force,
who is The-Oneness-Of-All-Life.
When we shared The-Life-That-Never-Dies
we made our Tribe to grow the earth.

Before the storm passed,
all who were ill
or had lost their teeth,
walked naked into the Death-Wind.

With Mother,
they fell asleep in gentle darkness;
fulfilling their moons.

Their spirits were never lost, for the white crystals
gathered and melted them into sun drops;
which Earth-Mother drank.

For every drop,
new life came-up in The-Season-Of-Growing-Things.
What she held in storage was the overflow of her thankfulness;
which she poured out freely.

These were the water trails
which filled the lakes or answered the Gathering-Water's call
to come on home.

This death-power
was in everything we ate and drank.
We shared it with All.

Taking this power to ourselves,
as a gift of peace,
our life stories became the hill grass.

Putting our feet in nature's moccasin prints,
we slowly danced with her,
until we became part of the chilling cold.

She brought us rest.

It was a season for staying still.
No work was done while Mother slept.
Our house cleaning was done only after dark.

The forest slept in simple, leafless dignity
beneath a white blanket of healing power.
The water wore a firm cold robe
to keep itself protected.

The animals put on heavy furs;
many slept in the ground.
Eagles and geese followed their magical visions
and flew toward the sun.

Darkness rested longer on the earth.
Shadows shuffled more slowly behind.
The sun was taking longer journeys each sleep.

It was a chance to be quiet
and to risk the silence of All-Mystery.

In the gentle stillness,
we found wisdom.
She was our strength.

We found our renewal in Mother's slumber.
The-Great-Change-Maker-Which-Evolves-In-All-Things
rested on us in quiet peace.

In emptiness
our creative desires
became disciplined by submission.

Spirit rocked us in earth's cradle valley
and Mother suckled us with care.

We yielded to the death of grass clumps,
bent beneath cold flakes,
and surrendered to the silence of falling clouds,
as they long-covered the land.

We found happiness in wind drifts
and joy in the singing crystals.

With dried berries,
on the sleeping bushes,
we opened ourselves to the Bite-Wind.

Its burning breath stung our hearts.
Its medicine purged us
with cleansing cold.

From fur cap to moccasin feet,
its power-tingle
chased away any life we tried to hold.

Its magic,
pulling us toward death-emptiness,
was our only chance for life;
it could not be overcome or avoided.

When we tried no more to hold on,
and our desire to live had gone,
we knew that magic was having its way:
Cold-Power was walking through us.

We knew this medicine power,
for Earth-Mother had the clay flesh of her body
pulled from her rock bones by glacial cutting.

NADA

This made her outlines.
Gouges plowed her ravines.
Scrapings made her mountains.
Avalanches scoop-cut her earth-shore borders.

We knew them all,
for crystal prints were our heritage,
and the flesh of our bodies
were the star dust specks
around which each water crystal gathered.

Wind medicine pushed through each star speck
which had swirled together to make us a body.

In the Death-Wind,
we were dust creatures,
spinning in obedience
to powers over which we had no control.

These were star powers,
calling us by name.

Once we received the cold under our skin,
its power upset everything,
and death became our cleansing.

Like moving mists
from the formless deep,
wind medicine blew through us,
restoring and healing us for death.

We peeked from under our animal's skins,
and ventured onto the deer cut trails,
leading from sheltered woodland thickets.

Believing that our hunger
could be met by eating their flesh,
we became their death-bringer.

Our family fed us
when we were hungry.

But the Bite-Wind was in them too;
and having given their lives to Great-Change-Maker,
they simply let themselves move beyond death.

We called our hunting trips, "funerals."

With wolverine mind,
we tracked our game as brave hunters.
Openly trading life for life,
we took the power
of our antlered relatives,
as the death we were soon to share.

Yes,
we did it with ritual respect and gratitude,
offering their blood and liver,
as thanks to The-Mover-Of-All.
"Hai!"

NADA

Their life power became our omen,
and we knew that oneness with our dead family
was but a wing stroke away!

My people ate the living power
we shared with our Ancestors,
now in animal form.

We accepted All as our family,
knowing that our brothers and sisters
walked naked into the woods
just ahead of us,
to fulfill their lives.

One thing was sure:
We had received the medicine
to restore our Mother's wholeness.

Rabbit followed pheasant.
Then came vegetable roots,
along with dried fish and fruits;
each one was a different Spirit form.

In the quiet darkness of our wakefulness
we must have asked
whether our earth family was more wise than we,
to surrender so easily to Spirit.

Fish and game were our flesh and blood,
and after eating our family member,
I remember listening to them whisper in my ears.

Sister deer chose her hunter,
and shared her body,
to teach us how to be gentle.
She reminded me that Spirit is kind
and takes care of those who walk in step with her.

Dried berries taught me
that full abundance is freely provided;
just as dew drops.
The dyes which the berries provided,
when their lives were crushed,
were signs of shared joy.

Root vegetables taught me
to hold my earth place.

Salmon left her home,
beneath the Great-Waters,
to teach us about change.
She said:
  *"Our growth comes
  when the moon shifts its shadow."*

She taught us
to heart-trust Moon-Spirit.
Eating the powder of her crushed bones,
we became strong.

Little rabbit's gift was play.
  "All life,"
  he said,
  "is to be a delight."

He also whispered:
 *"Having fun is Over-Spirit
 expressing Itself in laughter."*

So, each animal's trail
followed it to our death.

In the quiet dignity of white-cold,
we danced our power animals.
Wearing their furs,
we played out the mystery of their lives;
head and horns raised proudly,
we lived out the power of their unseen force.

Neither human or beast,
we acted out our family's blood-spirit.
With a quiet water drum
we danced one by one-
then all together:

Fast and gentle antelope,
strong and fearless buffalo,
wise-fool coyote,
sharp-eyed eagle,
quiet and ferocious cat
brave and fierce wolf:

All one great spirit.

Sometimes the smaller animals were attacked
by larger critters,
but rescued by another creature.

These silent blood-dramas
were to show the unbroken circle of All-Life,
which we shared;
wild forces and disciplined powers.

Should any animal try to break from our circle,
they would be pulled back
by the power of the central dancer,
the female power,
which draws all into obedience
and remakes their lives.

This invisible force
is the Life-Mystery
which pulls the dancer
from any desire to be separate.

It is the wild-strength
of each dancer's animal.

Our lessons were so powerful
we had to take off our masks
to know we were people.

So, I learned of death medicine
and received praise for being a great hunter.
My arrows stitched our worlds together.
I found my desire for adventure grew and grew.

Then one day,
when Sun had passed its peak,
several of us were hunting along Cougar-Pass-Trail.
We stopped to let our horses blow,
where we could look out over the lake and tall forest.
My pony over stepped a steep bank.

Down the rocks we spilled,
under and on one another.
Sprawling,
at last,
in the bottom of the ravine.

I was thrown outside myself.
I lost my trail
and gave myself to the whirling emptiness.
My inside head sounded like swans eating the clouds;
a sound made
when we rubbed our foreheads
with our finger tips.

My pony dead,
my body broken and battered;
we both said 'hello' to Dark-Silence.

II.

THE-GREAT-FORCE

My friends skinned the pony
and wrapped my bloody body in his hide,
hoping that our spirits,
mixed-together,
would bring me from my tangled thought-wandering.

Arriving in camp,
Power-Man stretched me on the pony hide.
My broken bones were set
with straight willow sticks.
and wet raw hide,
so, it would dry firm to my flesh.

On my shoulder cuts
he stretched spider webs
and blew puff-ball powder
in the running blood.
Then he put on bird down
to mend the tear,
and draw sky power into my open muscles.

NADA

My feathers looked like wings
too weak to flap.

For my legs,
he chewed some hemlock bark
and put it on like mud,
to dry up my fast running blood.

My head was toward Land-Of-Cold-Wind.
My dream-energy was toward my body,
seeking to find itself
and to bring my thoughts home.

The women with whom I had been sexual
during The-Death-Wind-Dance,
came to the sacred lodge
and sat around me in sky clothes,
chanting my power song;
making my spirit present,
as a trail finder.

They sat,
with their bodies straight up,
moving one shoulder forward
and then the next.
It was like wind
rocking strong lake reeds.

After three days,
they rubbed me with red paint,
blown through a crane's wing bone,
to bring me the power to be strong.

Their hearts were beside me.
They shared power from the life-chambers
of our unborn children.

The touching of my body,
and the gentleness of their chant,
brought fast healing.

In seven sleeps my body was together
and I was stumbling
in fog thought;
trying to see through hanging mists
in the dark woods of my pain.

I could hear them calling,
and just as Sun was breaking through,
they made a special ceremony;
offering me
as a living gift,
to Earth-Mother.

After blowing sage smoke over my body
with an eagle's wing,
to purify my life,
Power-Man offered sacred herbs
to the world-directions.

He then took a dirt pinch
between his thumb and finger,
letting it fall into the blowing wind.

By this he showed
that I was nothing without Spirit's power.
Then they cut the leather straps,
keeping my arms and legs pulled tight.

My body paint was scrubbed off
with cedar bark and raccoon grease.
Ptarmigan liver was put on my forehead,
to show me how to survive the cold season.

While pine knot torches were lit,
to honor our Ancestors,
the women rubbed me
with my own breeding juice.

The courageous men,
who had brought me to the lodge,
took the torches and
silently carried me to a cave
where the Grizzly was cold-sleeping
with her suckling cubs.

When we arrived at our Ancestor's cave,
they did not look inside,
because there might be wandering ghosts.

I was little awake.
I could see that Sun was a bow shot
above the sky edge,
and wondered how I would find my way
beyond this day.

My friends pushed me
toward Grizzly-Mother's warmth,
as if I were a stranger coming at night,
uninvited.

They quietly left,
knowing that when her milk passed through me,
I would be accepted as her own.

Wind was prowling around
in the dark cave emptiness.
I was shaking full-body,
from fear and cold.

My heart was running like an antelope.
Finally, it slowed down
and I found a calm quiet.

In my traveling wakefulness,
I looked at the dream-path I must walk.

The beginning step was to find an extra nipple
on a mother from whom my tribal life
would never have allowed me to learn.

Everything had to leave:
My desires,
fears,
and tribal role.

To risk anything,
when my customs and traditions fell silent,
took big-courage.

All I had was who I was alone,
and any sense of me hid in the fog,
like a bad dream.

Even as mother-bear reached out her big paw
and pulled me close to her,
she was Death-Wind tough.

She demanded all my courage
and asked for more.
She made the same demands from her purring cubs.
If I were to be part of this family,
Cold-Power must run in my blood.

Our training began
in deep cave-sleep silence.
Even here,
with the savage untamed,
death stood as a hero.

The ground on which mother's paw came to rest
trembled from her power;
so, it must do for me!
    Hai!

Weight did not shake the earth where she walked,
or tear the logs which she explored;
it was power.

In the silence which swallowed all sound,
she made us deal with this power.
She taught us not to limit it,
but to act from strength,
which, does not turn upon itself.

She taught us
that Mystery-Emptiness
is the beginning of everything.

This training could happen only in dark silence,
where there was nothing to pull at our attention.

It destroyed all who glanced aside.

She taught us to watch only unmoved movement.

In this silent place
is where everything happens.

We learned that earth is
not the soil on which we walk,
nor is it the water in which we swim.

It is not the air we breath
or Sun's ground warmth.

Earth-Mother is alive.
These other things
are only her shadows.

Her life is the power of all that lives.
"This,"
said mother bear,
"is the basis of everything we do.
Nothing else."

By now I was full awake.
I choked with the sour smell of bear,
not to mention the smell of the cave,
which trapped our breath.

I was not easy about suckling
from an animal my people spoke of as,
"The-Great-Force."

Her milk had healed my muscles,
but my body hurt with pain.
I would live.
But for what?

Moving from fog-sleep to being bright-awake
was a big jump.
In dream-sleep I dealt with power.

While awake,
I dealt with pain.
Which was real,
was like walking through night bog mists.

Trying to find who I was,
made me very lost.

Mother's paw rested over my heart.
Its weight sometimes crushed my wind.
I wanted to find my people.

But with my new earth-place,
'my people' seemed to include All;
maybe even the planet herself!

I had no 'where' to crawl.
This thought was like welcoming a strange brother.
Just then my mother's snout nuzzled my rump.
I snuggled in.

I could not stay perched on the edge of awake.
But to be as people think,
was like hopping on one foot;
I never got very far.

Finally,
I found that the dream-sleep of vision-journey
worked for me.
It let me learn from mother
and yet be calm during our cave rest.

My thought became easy,
like leaves which rest
after a storm,
when the wind is still.

As I became what was demanded,
I developed endurance-discipline.

NADA

I stayed in a vision-trance
for what seemed like
all the moons which would be mine.

III.

GUARDIANS-OF-POWER

Mother was not what anyone would call, *'easy'!*

Her watchful eye was difficult to escape.
Not only did I have much to learn,
I had a lot to unlearn.

For example,
she taught us that people are heavy water:
Not bodies,
but moving water power.

They are together like water drops,
which have dust specks
that are held and united by liquid.

People call these specks their bodies.
We Bears saw people as power drops,
all poured together.

NADA

She also taught us
to not focus our eyes.
We were to look out of our eye-edge
and not at anything straight ahead.

This way,
we saw everything as easy as
an eye blink.

Our actions were done with no thought.
We acted only from our inside life-force.

We were to watch for movement.
For the One-Who-Evolves-In-All,
taught us how to change.

Action is Great-Spirit's life power.

Nothing else mattered for us.
Whatever could most change
had the most power.

Air and water had more power than land,
but less than thinking.

Air,
mother told us,
is softer than water
and carried a different light layer.

She also said,
that what people call *'things'*
were only shadows.

Their emptiness-designs gave them appearance.
What made them real was not seen.

This was the difference between power and its shadow.

We were taught to act on power
and not on its shade.

For example,
hunters who knew their unseen,
were very powerful.
If they did not,
they were very weak.

Mother was strict about our knowing this,
and dug in her long claws
to teach me where I heart learned.

She did not care what I did with my brain.
It was my heart and my rump which
were her big care.

Just when cave air was all sucked out,
she pushed us from the cave
and into the cold.

NADA

I nearly drowned in fresh air,
but Might-Wind gave me endurance strength.
I had no fur
and very little fat by which to keep warm,
something mother never seemed to notice
for a heartbeat.

Neither did she look at my hobbled steps,
as I learned to walk and run again.

What she saw,
and most hit me for,
was watching shadows rather than power.

She was very cruel about this.

Once when I was looking at shadows,
she scratched a hole in my breeding basket.

She was so tough
it injured my cub brother for life.
This happened when we were playing
with power turned upon itself.

It was her way of saving his life,
for Thunder-Maker threw fast sky fire
and smashed the rock,
sending us all rolling downhill.

Just after this,
the smell of new cold was in the air.
Soon white flakes
were racing to the ground.
So, we went back to our cave lodge
for another moon cycle.

But we were more active.

Our activity had to do with
learning Bear-Tribe skills.
These were:

1)When to walk on all fours
and when to stand on our hind legs.
    Of the three of us,
    I had the most difficulty.

    Balance from our birth scar
    was what we had to learn.
    From this scar,
    we knew our Earth-Mother.
    This is where our lives were tied to her.
    It was here we stayed in touch with her.

    Mother-Bear said:
        "Sometime, we might get killed
        for how we use this tie;
        but we are life that never goes away.

How we are
is not our final Being.

Life is always on death edge,
So, we do not fear for survival.

When on all fours,
we are nearest life
and when we stand up,
we are nearest death."

2)How to play.

When it came to play,
I was always lacking.
My mouth was too small,
my skin was never tough enough,
and, with no fur,
I got scratched easily.

Since my pony's death,
my arm did not work well.
My underside and breeding basket were too available.
So, our wrestling left my neck to the ground
more often than extended above my playmates,
my belly exposed
rather than raised above theirs,
and being peed on or humped from the rear
in teasing games from my brother and sister.

Our play was rough-strong;
especially since brother's injury,
when he had to take his place after our sister.
It was hard to like the family order,
or its discipline.

3) The nature of danger
and what to do with it.

We were told that our big difficulty
came from not giving attention.

Aliveness is only for one breath.

In our one-breath-life,
we were to hear only our inside voice.

From this power
we learned our strength,
endurance,
and skills.

While I was trying to learn this,
mother bit my shoulder so hard
her tooth cut my fall-scar.
It was a deep bite.
But it undid whatever kept me from full reach,
and stopped my bear skills.

4)How to bring peaceful order.

We were Chief-Of-Land-Animals.
So, we had to keep things in balance.
Earth-Mother had appointed us,
   "Guardians-Of-Power."

To learn this,
we left our lodge.

Mother told us:
   "Power is very small.
   The little is often not seen,
   but has big results."

She also said:
   "Power is very simple.
   It is our breathing."

In the cold mountain air,
we could see the white puffs of our breath clouds.

She told us:
   "Breathing is the only power there is.
   The sky of Great-Over-Spirit,
   the earth of Great-Mother,
   the force of all living things
   is moving breath."

IV.

GREAT-CHANGE-MAKER

One frosty dawn,
when Sun had driven its arrow shaft into our cave,
to knock apart the inside darkness,
we went to the stone sky-touchers.

They had stood for many moons above the trail
where my journey
to our cave lodge had begun.

White crystals were deep in the pinnacle cracks.
But Sun shined bright
and a warm Chinook-Wind blew over us.

In the melting off-run,
a small water ran through a stone crack
on the up-side of the sky-touchers.

We watched the trickle water;
mother said that it was power.
By the seventh sleep I had little interest in *'power.'*

That night
a Bite-Wind came slow-moving across the land,
driving us back into our cave.
It froze the stream we had been watching.

When next we saw it,
water was not dripping from the ice-stabbers.
We circled up hill to watch.

Suddenly there was a deep earth-thump;
like when a rabbit warns the others.
Then two of the sky pinnacles slid,
like one hand over the other,
tipped and spilled.

Stones filled the ravine
and went onto the next ridge.
Boulders rolled to the lake,
smashing holes in its hard, clear blanket.
The echo moved from canyon to canyon,
as we snuggled near to mother.

When we ambled to the lake,
we could see that the stone holes,
already had a thin clear layer
feathering over the water;
healing the tear.

The feathers grew and grew
pushing the water.

Mother told us:
>*"Water feathers,*
>*like bird feathers,*
>*fluff in the cold.*
>*Wherever you see them fluff*
>*you see power*
>*writing Spirit's name,*
>*as light crystals.*
>*They are the breath marks*
>*of Great-Change-Maker-Which-Moves-In-All-Things."*

>*"Feather-puffs moved the mountain!"*
I whispered to my sister.

She nipped my leg and we were off,
running across the boulder-rock hillside.

Mother stopped beside a big stone,
that looked like it was about to run down hills.
By stepping on a limb,
she moved it from the boulder's edge front,
and sent it jumping down the canyon,
smashing out of sight.

>*"Power at rest,"*
mother told us,
>*"is its holding place.*

>*We must learn*
>*how it is let go,*
>*if we are to be Earth-Power-Guardians."*

"How do we know waiting power?"
I asked.

*"To know this
you become the Death-Cold.
You allow the feather fluffing of cold and warm
to make you big and little.*

*Power is always held in cold
and let go in warm.*

*Never try to make it happen
or you will disturb its friendship.
That would be your end."*

You do not control Earth-Mother's breathing power.
You become the one through which this power happens.

Even with warm sunshine days,
the nights were sharp cold.
The last storm of the season slid from the sky
and held us in our cave mouth.

For the next few sleeps,
sky spilled feather flakes.

As we watched,
I asked about sky power
along with earth and water power.

Mother told us
that air carried power
which was less hard and heavy,
so, it was fast and not very even;
like lightning and the night-dancing sky-lights.

She said
that the living land
was made of power-dust.

Everything is made from Earth's breathing patterns.
All changes are her power in us.

Our tie with her
gives us life.
We are her power shadow
just as earth is the shadow of Mother's ancient force.

Once this was becoming clear to my thoughts,
Mother-Bear violently pushed me out of the cave
and guarded our lodge opening

My choice was the Bite-Cold power
or the bite of her mouth.

I took the cold Death-Power,
and lay,
face down, on all fours,
outside our lodge.

She watched me,
as I lay there
breathing Death-Cold.

My desire to sleep was strong.

But I heard Great-Change-Maker say:
  "Find Mother's breath,
  as the pounding drum of your inside dance.
  She comes to your body with death.

  Give up your shadow,
  so that it can rest
  while you explore the trails of your new moons."

Death-life came,
just as when night east the moon.
As the cold dawn-wind
blew soft air up the canyon,
I felt fire in my blood.

My journey was like a going-out-tide.
Only there would be no return.

Star music played across the trees
and sounded like the chanting
of every tribal dance which ever was.

My heart began to sing.
People welcomed me,
as a brother coming from a long journey.

They were across a deep river from me.
Down this river floated my birth mother,
father,
and our family lodge.
My friends followed one by one.
My pony came washing by,
and mother bear with her cubs;
then my body.

These had been my earth snares,
keeping me from magic-power.
When everything floated away,
I cut a willow
and made a river-spirit-flute.

I blew the star-music
which still played in my head.
It was like air-breath
over all that lives.

It froze the river with a strong robe.
I crossed to the other side,
still playing my flute.

Then I blew one shattering light blast.

It felt like a new born sun at dawn.

It rolled boulder rocks into the river,
which broke through its cold cover.

NADA

Water moved again.
I felt like one of the Otter-Tribe,
who was early
to put its nose through the top-river's new thaw.

No longer my body,
I was a one-note sunlight breath:
The medicine power
necessary to restore sacred life.

My destiny was Mystery.

V

POWER-GUARDIAN

In willow flats beside the river,
the sky was shining with young light.

It was early dawn;
the fertile light of new things;
when grass and trees renewed themselves,
as they danced along the pollen-path.

Sun filtered through catkin tails,
hanging on the alder branches,
and landed on the moss-bank
holding pink-white star flower,
    "Aii-ya!"

This new light
played with the minnows and water skippers.
It tumbled from steep spillways.

It caught the lichens,
in bright colored wind wisps.

It moved along the round-turn corners

and feathered itself
in purple thin shadows
worn under tree roots,
where stones washed the ripple waters.

Soft air carried shining insect trails,
and reflected slant filtered beams
riding on pollen-dust-wind.

It was an easy light,
which opened buttercups,
and teased the spear-nosed mosquito
from its under-water lodge.

It probed dandelion roots
and raised the curve-neck ferns.
It touched the frogs, snails and slugs.
It played with the otters
and danced with the cranes.

It made squirrels jump and critters run.
It flew the butterflies,
and sang a song
which sky circled eagles.

   "Power-Guardian,"
      I said aloud,
as I saw life awakening;
watched robins building nests
and deer giving birth to their young.

Field mice and coyotes ran free.
Hawks perched in the maple trees.

Long-beaked blood suckers sang
   "Tsi-ni-ni-ni,"
and fly-away bugs answered
   "Tsu-nu-nu-nu."

The river came from Land-Of-The-Rising-Sun.

I followed it toward the dawn;
in search of its beginning.

With Sun
I climbed higher and higher.

The river stream showed me mountain sheep
walking beside their trail rocks.
Eagles flew high,
watching my journey.

Entering a deep, skinny ravine,
it began to press in on me
until the stream became my only trail.

The water was very cold.

I wondered if I could stand up long enough
to get to a rock outcropping,
or to a gravel bar along the swift stream.

When my body was cold blue,
I came to a big lake with no shore.

Water was spilling into it from the rim canyon.
My only choice was to go back the way I had come.

Water flows down,
So, I made it out easier than going in.

My body was a deep cold purple
and the going-down-sun offered small heat.

As the red sun-shadows were running away,
I saw rising steam from a close-by hot spring.
By the time I hobbled to it,
dawn and dusk had joined
to become blackness
and Sun had gone behind the earth.

Even with the water smelling like an unhappy skunk,
sleep came fast.
When I opened my eyes,
it was to the sound of snake rattle-tails.

I had invaded their territory without permission.
Now there was no excusing myself.
   "Okay brother,
   I'll be out of your way in a tail's shake."

As I jumped into the sky,
three poison mouths lunged to where I had been.
They undid themselves from the over thrust
made by my sky climb.

Returning to the ground,
I landed on the head of grandfather snake;
injuring his mouth.
Both sun-ray fangs were broken
and one poison sack was poked through.
The other snakes slithered away!

I took serpent as my traveling friend,
so he would not die
because of my lack of attention
to Snake-Tribe customs.

He was longer than I was tall,
but I put him around my neck
and we became close brothers.

For two moons I caught mice for him to eat.

Mother bear did not teach me about throat learning
but brother serpent did,
and his training began
as soon as he was around my neck.

He called me his friend
and told me I had learned only *"death ways."*
He said that I must learn the *"life trail."*

I asked how he knew I was ready.

He said that my sky leap
to avoid his bite
had been my test.

For the privilege of teaching me,
he had taken my heel stomp.
He went on to say that I was now with him,
"and how can one know any better
than when guide and guided are together?"

"Of course,"
he admitted,
"it is never clear who needs the guidance."

"At least he has a sense of humor!"
I thought.

VI.

THROAT-LEARNING

"So, you are going to the top-waters."
He stated,
as we climbed the black-roasted rim rock
which holds earth power
and contains the records of far gone away life.

It was good for my foot-place
that the frozen white-cold was on the land,
like a rabbit-skin blanket.

The mountain folds were steep drops
and the canyons jumped straight up
in front of my face.
My head felt dizzy.
I thought I might fall over the edge
with the easiest wind breath.

Near the top,
where the earth was as wide as day light,
squirrel chattered a welcome.

There were two springs side by side.
Snake told me that the hot one
came from earth-center.
The cold one
was drawn from the lake by Cedar,
whose branches had over-spread the land for many moons
and whose roots were earth deep.

In reverence,
I lay on my stomach,
waiting for what I did not know.

When tree spoke,
it was a low drum-rumble voice.
    "Welcome little one!"

I was home!
… at least for a while.

The opening for our rock-ledge overhang
was toward Where-Comes-The-Light.

So, tree and the two springs were in close sight.

Even though white cold
held its blanket close over the land,
the water springs attracted many animals.

An eagle's nest was high in the tree.

Mountain-top had its own traditions,
which snake was careful to observe,
as he began talking with me about, 'LIFE.'

Usually we talked
after Sun had reached middle sky,
because serpent was very slow
to free himself from the cold nights.

Tree shared my mornings;
even this day.

I found that I heard him best
when sitting on his roots
with my back laid in a gentle curve.

What I heard was his deep silent whisper,
as a voice speaking out of dense darkness.
Then I saw earth from his top branches

As I looked down,
I learned deep inside,
to be part of her.

Tree was the magic moccasins for my view.
He told me:
        "It is because trees
        are earth's life connectors with sky."

So,
this early morning,
as Dawn pulled Sun along its path,
it touched the cedar branches pushing against the open sky.

Tree was so old he did not dance,
he only sang.

I smiled at his dignified way,
and let my breath go to the wind.

I could feel tree fluids up-drawing me.
We became one life.
Star wisdom was in us.

While tree and I shared sky color,
Great-Change-Bringer-Flowing-In-All
covered my head
with a cedar bough circle
and eagle feathers.

I still remember the funny rainbow songs we sang.

One went:
   "When no beginning was
   we were one;
   In emptiness
   there was only us.

White light moved star dust here and there,
we hung a circle for the sun.
We set no edge for dawn or dusk,
but took them to our heart.

We sang the song
which made the critters, one by one.
Life came floating by
and,
with the moon,
we picked her from the sky.

We held her near,
and shared our dreams.
That's as far as earth has come,
or,
so,
it seems!"

Tree laughed wildly at our joke.
Snake thought it a little childish,
but tolerated it.

As we sat beside the hot spring,
his long body around mine,
he held me near,
enjoying our warmth.

After a bit, he said:
    "Life is Invisible-Spirit,
    making Itself known in living things.
    You are the Life in all things."

63

I stopped him and said:
    "My way to learn is down-on-earth.
    No uppity talk for me!"

Tightening himself around my throat,
he told me to feel my breath.

There was no choice.
Every air-suck now had a sound.
    "Listen to your breathing,"
he told me,
    "and you will hear Life-power."

I remembered mother bear's lesson
and nodded my head.

    "Life seemed to be
    your need to take a breath.

    She is neither your breath or your need.

    She is your demand to be you."

With the pressure on my neck,
snake held me
somewhere between no breath and stupor.

I felt like I was being born.
Thought was like a child
peeking around a tree.
I came to a vision-trance,
where I could breathe Life herself.

Then I heard snake say:
"Now you are pure Life,
as a breath of light."

"What a comment!"
I thought.

Then I thought no more.

VII.

OLD-RED

Spirit was my mind-fullness.
Everything was silent.

When I woke up,
moon was standing in the sky
waiting for darkness to get there.

It never did
because the moon just shined more and more light.

My feet were in the hot spring.
My head was in the cold spring.
Snake was eating a mouse.

I realized that for me to understand 'Life,'
I must become the power I was to know.

This meant living in dream-vision
as my life way.

Anything else would be death.

I looked at serpent.
He was circle coiled in a blue-red fire.

I looked at tree,
splashed in a deep gold.
Cloud colors were joy-flickering from him,
as a high-burning fire.

I looked at sky
and heard laughter twinkling in the stars.

I looked at myself
and there was a glowing power inside,
like a teepee fire at night.

Earth-Mother's pleasure
sat on the full-moon.

The spring at my feet was red.
At my head, it was blue.

I knew I had to learn everything over.
This time it was to be *'Life-wisdom'*
rather than *'death-lessons.'*

To start,
I had to learn
that emptiness is Change-Bringer's only force.

It is made of Great-Mystery.

To know this unseen power,
only the strong raw-hide bow string
of my heart-mind
could get me to where I had to be.

Earth-Mother was so happy with my training
that she sent Night-Lark to tree perch
and sing my discoveries to the critters.

As snake and I lay on our soft tree boughs,
under the rock ledge,
I wondered how all this
was going to happen my life.

Had I known,
I could not have slept;
the joy would have been too big.

As Dawn was making its way down Morning-Star-Trail,
I decided to share the new sun with *'Old-Red,'*
a name I decided to call Cedar.

Serpent grunted for me to *"en-trance"* myself,
which was an order from him,
this cold morning!

Just as I sat on Red's foot,
Sun tangled his top branch-feathers.
An energy-whoosh shot up Red,
which felt like Great-Wind
biting my stomach.

It shoved me with such power
that I lost where I was
in the sky's top reaches.

Old-Red caught me on the way down,
just as my father did when I was a child.

Having looked so many moons away
was a bit crazy making,
but I smiled as best I could.

Meanwhile,
Cedar was humming deep inside.

   "Mighty One."
I said.
   "Please let me to see 'Life' today."

Great-Cedar trembled in deep silence;
then we were beside the river,
in a canyon, far below.

   "What do you see?"
I felt his question.

   "I see a flowing stream'
part of the Gathering-Waters.
I see beauty in its ripples
and power moving silently in its deep pools."

"No! No!
What do you see
from your heart-vision?"

"I see wind running along power trails."

"Yes! Yes! Go on!"

"It is breathing Earth-Mother into action."
I continued.

Old-Red spoke
and said:
"Rivers are life-stream shadows
in the growth change of Earth-Over-Spirit.
They are light-stream-life-lines,
like the red rivers of your blood,
and the flow of my sap.

Their shadows are scratched
on and under Mother's land."

"What of the Gathered-Waters?"
I asked.

"They are also shadows;
shadows of Mother's life carrying power.
They are the source of all things."

I was in awe-wonder,
and asked Red if we could return to the mountain.

"Spirit's mind shadows,
scratched on earth,"
I kept repeating.

When snake came by,
we went to the springs.

"Water,"
I said,
"is a Spirit shadow;
earth's life lines."

"I know."
He responded.
"Water is sacred.
It is life renewing presence.
That is why we pour Mother the first drink,
when we are thirsty."

"But I thought water was real stuff."
I blurted out.

"It is everything you thought.
It's just that Spirit is so much more!"
His quiet comment rattled deep in my throat.

I was silent
until long tree shadows
moved across the mountain springs,
where water was over spilling me.

NADA

When I looked for snake,
I found him curled at Old-Red's foot.

I sat down
and we watched darkness come quietly
over the land edge,
to fill all the canyons,

Finally,
it covered everything from sunset to sunrise.

VIII

SKY-POWER-KEEPER

Sleep-Bringer was late.

I had a sense I was snake,
he was me,
and,
together,
we were Old-Red.

Everything was falling together.

Moon seemed to pour water from Earth-Mother's spring.

Wolves threw their voices past the trees
and made their chanting
wind-ride from our ledge rock.

Our cave
mountain echoed wolf spirit's voice.

When morning-light arrived,
I stomach crawled to Old-Red
and settled into my seat.

When Sun touched Red's top,
I felt the power whoosh again.
It threw me into the sky
like air thunder.

Eagle whistled a shrill call
and caught me on her back.

We circled higher and higher
on Spirit's wind trail.
Earth seem fuzzy as we climbed.
I was tiny against the sky.

    "Eagle."
I said.
*"Tell me of the land.
It must be a shadow!"*

She laughed,
for she was Sky-Power-Keeper
and Great-Spirit's medicine bird,
who guarded air sacredness.
She dive-plunged.
    *"Ai!
A shadow!"*

She had eyes that looked through things.

    *"Was I mistaken?
If water is a shadow
then why not land?"*

Our flight leveled,
at the rim rocks.
We floated low,
as if preparing for a change wind.
Her wings stretched full
over the canyons and steep mountain slopes.

    "A shadow."
She repeated.
    "And what is a shadow?
It is a cloud;
but land is no cloud.
Water is a shadow;
but it is not land."

She sharp turned so much
I almost slid off.

    "Child,
give me no foolishness!"
She laughed.

    "I am yours."
I called back over the whistling winds.
    "But I tell you,
I want to know your wisdom about land."

She hunched,
as though to make a direction change.

"Land is the magic shade
of Spirit's image."
She said.
"It is a water balance.

Water is Spirit's shadow
and Mother's life power.

Land is the shade of Spirit presence.
It is the stuff of all things.

Land and sea are images of The-Mysterious-One
who lived in the Sun."

"Then who are we?"
I asked with a boldness which surprised us both.

"We are beauty expressions of The-Mysterious-One.
So, we are mostly water."

This did not fit together.

But we had landed,
and eagle wanted the quiet of her sacred space.

I slid down the tree
to where I was sitting,
and found snake coiled around my feet.

"Why is eagle so stingy with words?"
I asked serpent.

He laughed.
"Be glad she speaks to you at all,
she hardly ekes a word to me!"

"Snake.
What are the living things of earth?"

"We are light-life,
of which Sun is a shadow.

We come from Spirit
just as sunbeams from Sun.

Everything is one."

"This is why, you and I,
were the same last night!"
I replied.

There was a long silence.

"I thought so too."
Serpent finally said.

"I also thought wolf
would never stop howling it to Moon,
who poured out the stream of our friendship
to become the morning dew."

With each sleep,
I felt more and more at home.

I became the opening flower petals,
as we followed the sun trail.
I was the eagle scream
far up in the sky blue
and the warm-wet of hot spring.
I became the living mountain rocks
and the roots of every plant.

This was more than feeling that I was like them.
Our spirits' together mingled.

I knew the word as each lupine,
paintbrush
and sunflower.

Life herself was our days.

When I was becoming Old-Red,
The-Season-Of-Growing-Things was turning
toward The-Season-Of-The-Hot-Sun.

From him,
I learned that trees
are Change-Bringer's connection
with earth creatures.

The rings,
inside each tree,
are worn sun trails.

They are the markings of change.

Red became my sky-power bridge.

Life clothed us with Mystery.

We shared the light,
as it ran through our outstretched limbs.
We stood boldly on the mountain,
feeling the rain fall gently over us
and the clouds cover our eyes.

The winds sent great forces through us,
and we became a pathway
over which Change-Maker brought blessings
to the critters.

Old-Red's many seasons
allowed me to stand in the star moons of change
and watch earth's growth.

As a path-bridge between earth and sky,
between Mother and Great-Spirit,
we were privy to their love.

Light and darkness danced through us,
as a joy trail.

Animals and birds sheltered in our presence,
to rear their young
and to live their passing suns.

These were days of glory silence;
observing Earth-Mother nodding toward Sun.

Trees got dressed in new leaves;
plants began to sky dance,
animals ate Mother's abundant gifts.

Then,
one day tall clouds,
carrying the voices of lightning people,
moved across the sky.

They pulled fire from the earth
and wound it like a lariat rope.
While they played many drums,
they shot sky-fire back to earth;
weaving earth-sky into a big basket.

As the talking clouds came near,
I could feel everything inside me move.

Red and I got ready for earth-sky
to become one power through us.

In the rain dance,
thunder drums played our medicine song.

Suddenly there was a big crash.
Fire fingers,
from deep in the earth,
stood with us,
and merged through us,
as a living power river,
pouring into the sky.
We became one mighty force.

Old-Red was pulled apart.

I was shattered into emptiness.

IX

BUFFALO-SPIRIT

We fell over the mountain cliff
and down the sky
wearing lightning power.

It was the top of Red which was torn off,
and I rode it
like a floating feather on the wind.

We landed in the ancient river,
which was bank-full and roaring,
with avalanche rain wash.

We hit so hard
that it shook me into sleep.
Red's limbs held me on the top waters.

In the changing shadows,
stars cradled me in sleep darkness.

When the early mists beamed the sun,
river returned my soul in the form of Eagle,
who lay dead beside me in Old-Red's branches.
A salmon was in her claws.

I ate her gift
and made her feathered skin my head cover.
Her spirit and mine
became like a wound-together honeysuckle vine.

From her spirit,
I learned the sky strength,
which was shining new light after the storm.

As spirit collected itself
in the drops which hung on things,
I gathered Old-Red's seed nubbins.

After eating four of them,
I planted the others in marsh mud
so that the new roots
could bind the river banks.

When the planting was completed,
I swallowed four gold pebbles
which were gathering sun along the river.

Then I celebrated my arrival on the Plaines,
by doing a song-dance
around a fire from Old-Red's branches.

After that,
day and night stood together,
for I could not sleep.
I even brewed a soft tea
from dried leaves of the night shade plant.

Nothing helped.

So, I danced and danced.

Sometimes animals joined me;
wolf or coyote,
stripe-face badger
silver foxes,
wag-tailed deer
long eared rabbits,
grouse drumming his own dance,
top-knot quail -
all celebrating Old-Red,
in reverent thanks.

On the last celebration day,
I was sitting on the river bank
breaking a stone;
Tock! Tock! Tock!
Red returned to me
as Black-Horn-Buffalo-Chief.

He lay down in the fire ashes
and wallowed for a long time.

Feeling Earth-Mother's strength,
he stood and said:
    "Take Old-Red's body.
    Make a canoe."

Hollowing and gouging,
burning and cutting at the heart wood,
I completed this task
by the beginning of The-Flower-Moon.

Each night,
as the blue-mist dusk
crawled down the mountains
and settled in the canyons,
Chief-Black-Horns returned
to spend his sleep with me.

When our canoe was ready he said:
    "My brother,
    you have proved yourself Mountain-Chief,
    now you must become full of prairie wisdom.
    Float down the river.

    It is the season of your fulfillment.

    Go.

    But take my robe as good medicine.
    My strength is yours,
    as you receive my breath.
    Take my wisdom.

Lead our Tribe as they are drawn by new food
and chased by the white crystals."

He lay down
and I drew his breath into my lungs.

Together we held the air.

Power stampeded through my body.
I felt great plain's strength.
It was the might of the Black-Horns,
who camped on these wind-swept lands.

Then I breathed out his breath
as a prayer:
 "Thank you Great-Chief.
  I have drunk your sacred life wind."

As I prepared his heavy robe,
I felt humble
with the power of his dignity.

 "What was this great venture
 for which Chief was willing to give me his life?"

I ate his liver.

When day was above our heads,
Old-Red,
Eagle,
Buffalo
and I
put-in below the falls,
for our venture to Land-Of-The-Prairie-Sun.

This land was our Mother-Who-Never-Dies,
and my venture there was a reminder
to go back to the open freedom of my childhood.

X

BLACK-HORN-TRIBE

From when the prairie moon was full
until it was old,
we floated like a river weed;
allowing the water's easy turns
to guide us through the sprawling flat lands.

The river moved in snake rhythms
through rabbit brush and long grass,
over trout pools and gravel wash.

The moon colored salmon had come home.

Many were climbing against the fast-water
or leaping up stream among the boulders.
Others were spawning in the shallow riffles.

River was life-full.

FACE-OF-THE-RISING-SUN

There was a small land in the white-waters,
where two rivers joined their lives.
A flock of split-tailed swallows dipped
and flew to the island;
preparing my way.

I banked the canoe,
where the voice of many waters was great.

I could hear nothing else.

Buffalo-Spirit led me to a tall mystery rock.

It was an Earth-Spirit
which looked like an old tree stump,
where Mayflies sky danced until they died.

I sat in the hot sun,
circled by the horizon,
and surrounded by willow stick slumps.

  "Listen."
  Said Buffalo-Spirit.
  *"Listen only to the singing waters.
  Become its voice."*

After not eating for many suns,
my silence put on bigger and bigger rocks,
until,
finally,
it smashed something inside me.

89

NADA

The hurt was so big
I found relief
only by being where Spirit things live.

Things seemed not to be where they were.

Instead of things,
I saw sacred space behind them;
radiance,
rather than forms.

I understood more than can be said.

Things disappeared.

Everything was made of Spirit
and stood closer than dreams.

I became the Invisible-One.

A butterfly,
whose wings came from the sunset,
landed on stump-rock,
gentle as an air breath,
a splendor spirit;
winged light-feathers,
The-Bringer-Of-Dreams.

She bowed and said:
    "Mystery-Chief,
    I would know how emptiness
    is truth guardian."

"Very well."
I said to this maker of words.
"Truth is sheltered
in the magic of your beauty."

Then serpent was there.
"How do you know?"
He asked.

"My heart,
where the traditions are written,
tells me."
I said.

Along came finch,
whose rich color filled my eyes.
"How is Mystery our open emptiness?"

"Your splendor keeps you from knowing
that Wisdom is your fulfilled Mystery."
I replied.

Then a hairy spider appeared,
whose bite could poison my body.
"How do you know?"
He asked.

"The sacred center,
where my legs meet the directions,
tells me."

Mother bear came to the rock
and,
with one swoop,
pushed me off.

She caught me a salmon to eat.

I had not seen her,
since I left our cave lodge.
My happy heart drummed with joy,
but I could not eat because of my vow.

> *"May you have happiness and health."*
> I said.

Then my parents arrived,
and were replaced by
Raven-The-Messenger-Who-Brings-Life.

When I was a child
we had grown to one another
like vines which are planted together.

Her eyes were like fire embers,
fanned in the night wind.
> *"How do you know?"*

> *"I do not know you."*
> I said.
> *"I let you fly from your basket-cage
> when I was a child.
> I look at you from far moons away."*

When she disappeared,
I was alone,
sitting on my buffalo robe.

In the changing black sleep-shadows,
I got lost
and asked for a courage-dream.

A living spirit-light,
from the prairie-grass-wind,
came to me.

She was more beautiful than words can say.
Her body was more wonderful than thoughts.
As she pounded my heart,
it became a living fire.

All of me was hungry for her.
Her magic movement
touched my deepest power.

Then I discovered
that this creature had two souls;
one man and one woman.

I was very upset.

    "Come,"
s/he said,
in a voice soft as the quail's.
I felt I could not hold back.
    "Your wisdom way
    is to become me."

NADA

From all of me,
I knew s/he spoke well.
But I would not let go.

The open prairie,
with one wind whisper,
was more than who I am:
An experience of deep Mystery,
a horror too much to say.

There was no room for me.

I could only guess how it was *"my"* way.

No wonder Raven had been
my last reminder of before-moons.
If I were to walk this adventure,
I must let go of all.

The magical prairie being
was asking for everything;
for life and death!

They were the same.

There were no differences.

Everything poured together.

Before The-Bright-Fire-Star
dipped to the edge of the prairie grass,
I sang my bravery song
and risked the courage of this challenge.

In a wing stroke s/he cut my skin
and drew blood:
A change sign!

The unspeakable sacredness of body cutting
meant sacrificing my entire life.

Sun reflected a rainbow
which swept away the clouds.
As I crossed this bridge,
I felt a new life.

It led me inside,
to the wordless fulfillment of myself.

Sucking a deep breath of flat-land-air,
I seemed to have a view block.

I looked through Spirit-eyes,
and saw super-natural powers;
light designs I had never known.

All things shined colors.

NADA

Flower colors changed during the day
and leaves became color heavy each night.
Grass color reflected earth,
while stone color shifted
in moisture and sunlight.
Buffalo glowed warm colors.

I joined them.
We played together,
enjoying our laughing shadows.

Earth was our delight.

The order of the stars ran through our lives.

We were the peace of Great-Mystery.

Turkey helped awaken each Dawn,
and with the dew still heavy on our robes,
we grazed on tender shoots
and drank beside the quiet stream.

In the warm sun
we dusted ourselves in the wallows
and enjoyed our earth closeness.

As I became brother to the Black-Horns,
we were led by the Spirit of the Chief
whose robe I wore.

I gave myself to the herd,
who listened to his council
and followed his wisdom.
He brought good fortune
and we grew strong.

Our earth place was very powerful.
Here is the wisdom which became our rules:

-All are equal.
-Receive peace.
-For all you use, share what you take.
-Harmony is good medicine.
-Trust All.
-Life Reverence.

The strongest bull
was given the breeding task.
The strongest cow
was given the herd-leading duties.
In Buffalo-Tribe,
we each had a role
which represented our sky-life.

We were on earth
the way we were with Spirit.

Our Tribe was so many
that we were like
the forest,
the grass
and the ants
who live in big Tribes.

At council meetings,
when I stood on top of our tallest buffalo,
on the highest ridge,
I could see that we stretched
from skyline to skyline.

As one life,
Spirit guided us,
or we could not have lived together in peace.

With Sun,
we lived in the open fields.
With Moon,
we dreamed in the sheltered hollows.

Peace settled over us
like a flock of birds.

We gave ourselves freely
to the wolves and coyotes,
to the birds and bears,
and to all others
according to our agreements.

The honor of sharing ourselves
showed our wisdom and care.

Even our buffalo droppings were scattered
such that they renewed the grass.
The-People-Tribe used them for fire.

From the Black-Horn-Tribe,
I learned the above-earth secrets.

PRAIRIE-DOG-TRIBE

The-Prairie-Dog-Tribe
traveled with the underworld spirits.
Little creatures with short hair
and high squeaky voices;
they also lived in a large Tribe.

I became one with each critter,
as we peeked from our burrows
and sang songs to eagles and coyotes.

Our rituals
let the sky birds and land animals know
which of us were honored to be food for them.
Usually the ones chosen
were the more fragile and fibrous.
They had prepared to be a food gift.

When one of us was blessed by being selected,
we went to the underground spirits
and celebrated the joy of this honor.
Over and over we sang:

"I want the eagles to eat my body.
I want the coyotes to eat my body."

It was good medicine,
and we would have breeding ceremonies
just so other of our offspring
could be so fortunate.

Coyotes and foxes,
cats and wolves,
snakes and bears,
all were Spirit-hunters,
for blessing us with change-life.

It was here,
I learned how to share life.

Each animal and plant,
(in fact, all living things),
shared prairie life.

The only things we did alone were:
Greet the early sun,
commune with the sweet earth
and meet the great silence.

It was always an adventure
to shift our life force.

Each prairie life was lived for all.
Our greatest courage act
was to give ourselves
to be eaten by the Great-Ones.

Insects rejoiced
as they died
to become part of change-life.

As plants,
we bore seeds for the Great-Ones.

In water,
we mixed our power
so that liquid held life
for the Great-Ones.

We carried strength
for we stood together
as one life force.

Our earth presence was a shadow,
a shadow lost at sunset.

What appeared to be death
was simply becoming part of
the endless journey.

This change was our prairie strength.

Breath-wind sang us sky-songs,
So, we always knew our place.

Each song was our life action.

XI.

WOLF-PACK

One morning,
down by the cottonwood place,
The-Wise-One told me to run with coyote,
as she made food rounds for her pups.

She welcomed me with suspicion.
When I became part of the family,
and finally, one of the prairie pack,
I found that this suspiciousness
came from coyotes being big pranksters.

Every night we moon howled,
    "Ah-ooo, Ah-ooooo"
and tried to mislead others
by throwing our voices
from other parts of the prairie.

Many times, we yelped, instead of singing,
so we could do it on the run.
While hunting,
we chased and bounded around
the rabbit brush.

We stalked quietly,
down wind from the critters we hunted,
and then pounced upon them with great flurry.

Style,
rather than conquest,
developed our wily boldness.

Alertness and agility
developed our courageous risk taking.

Our wolf cousins
put all this into detail,
and made our skills into a pack mind.

So,
once Wolf-Chief accepted me,
it seemed natural to move into the pack.

I developed a keenness
for thinking the thoughts of our prey.

We simply out-witted
whatever game we honored to take and eat.

In every part of our society,
we worked with one another in close discipline
and followed our leader in every detail.

Reverence for our Chief
was strong among the wolves.
But joining the pack
was very demanding.

I had difficulty throwing my thoughts away
and giving all of me to our Chief's demands.
While we were each different bodies,
we were one mind in all our activity.

The flowing together of my life with wolf spirit.
meant that I let go of everything I was.
My life got pushed together with the pack.
It smashed all traditions I had.

Letting go of the memory of my ancestor's memory,
I had nothing to go by.

It broke up all my thought.

My best letting go
was when I learned to howl.
  "Hu-Hu-Hu
  Hu-u-Hu-u-Hu-u!"

When I howled,
any trace of my past moons was heard
and the pack allowed only the present heart beat.

When Chief decided I could be trusted
to think only wolf thoughts,
we started our journey toward the setting-sun.

The-Season-Of-The-Hot-Sun was changing
to The-Season-Of-Colored-Leaves.

As we moved to higher hunting grounds,
Old-Woman blew and rattled the leaves.

The green prairie grass was ripe and brittle-brown.
It snapped under our feet.
When we came into the land that hunches into hills,
our discipline became strong.
The demands on us were very big.

   "Why the push?"
I asked Chief one day.
Her answer was an ear nip.
It tore a ragged cut.

Never again did I question her decisions.

After this,
I had to take trust tests.

The pack held me spread eagle
and attacked my throat,
until I stopped protect-twitching.

They nipped at my stomach,
inner legs
and breeding basket
until I stopped pulling back in pain.

NADA

These tests often continued from dawn
until half the sun was gone.
Sometimes their scratches lasted many sleeps.

Usually,
in late morning,
the pack licked my wounds
and we fell asleep together.
I was learning trust-discipline from them.

Some days we loped through the rock hills
until the sun was straight up in the middle.
It was hard work.
all of us were tired or torn.

We seemed to be under some outside demand.

As Day-Break-Star was bright
and touched lightly on the trees,
Chief took us to a high ridge
where earth powers met.

We ran along the sloping mountain thigh,
until we saw
where the prairie took a sky leap.

It was so high
that the cliff reached to us.

In the other direction,
a river cut through tall rough mountains,
which scratched their color from the clouds.

A wild river rushed and roared past us.
As it plunged through rib-rock gorge,
its white-water bubbled up;
scratching the sides with foam.

Then it fell over the cliff,
and crawled easily through the lowlands.

We were to swim these swirling waters.

As wolves,
we took another look at most things.

But we never questioned Chief's decision.
We simply followed in our pack order,
mine being last.

Underwater spirits caught me
and pulled on my legs.
When I finally struggled loose,
I had been washed far down stream.
I was only mid-stream
and had no pack member to follow.

Chief had made it to the other side.

She knew what had slowed me down.
I could feel her breath in my ear.
    *"Use your strength-discipline.
    Move quickly."*

With her guidance,
I could trust everything to her.
I swam with great power,
but river pulled me under in a deep sucking twist.

When I came to top-air again
I felt strong guiding thoughts-
the pack was with me!

Then I heard Chief say:
  *"Float.
  Just float."*

It was the last thing I heard.

River took my body
and threw it over the cliff.

Falling through the air,
spilling in the fine water mist,
I became part of river breath.
I floated on the soft breeze;
just as Chief had ordered.

When the falling water stopped,
I landed in a big puddle.

The splash knocked out my wind
and scattered my thoughts,
like a swarm of bees.

I lay there floating on my back;
just as Chief had ordered.

The-waters-moving-round
kept my body in the pool.

Dusk was gathering itself together
when my thoughts stopped going in every direction.
Sun was hiding among the far tree tops,
getting ready to go over the earth-edge.

I wolf-paddled to shore,
as if it were my last swim.

I was battered
and had no leg feeling.

As I stomach crawled across the sand pebbles,
I thought of snake
and laughed.
It awakened my first memory
since becoming part of the wolf pack.

Fortunately,
the straw-colored twilight was warm
and the cricket chirping night was short.
I could rely on Sun's return.
I gave praise to the weather.

My legs didn't feel anything,
So, I doubled my body into a sleep circle.

NADA

In the hazy darkness,
way up on the cliff top,
I heard the pack sending their voices
to the four earth directions-
calling for me.

They were far above.
It sounded like a dream-vision
echoing through spilling water
and wandering out over the prairie.

I started to call back,
but my voice got throat stuck.
I have never made that sound since.

After The-Star-That-Never-Moves lit its fire,
I never heard their calls again.

But sometimes,
even now,
I feel Chief very near.

XIII.

GATHERING-OF-MANY-WATERS

I awoke just as Day-Break-Star was
bringing strength-power to the day.

All things were shining with new life.

Dawn-wind was air floating its voice
like fireweed plumes.

Slowly the stars closed their eyes,
and the new-born day got greener.

A tall crane came out of the gathered hollow mists
and did a magic-dance beside me.
Then she flew away,
like a creature from the edgeless dawn.

As water mists flew before the rising sun,
a band of wild horses came to drink.
They could smell wolf on me
and shied away in restless fear.

NADA

Their Chief had hide scars
which looked like people writing.

He saw me against the moss bank,
opposite their drinking hole,
and snorted a warning.

Gently,
I whispered horse nickers to him.
He came near to get a look;
his proud mane and tail held high.

He seemed to dance,
like a spider on hot ashes.
Maybe that was from the rocks under his feet.

Moving from wolf mind to horse thoughts,
I felt how it would be to capture him.

He was ruled by freedom,
and I had to respect his pride.

Without people,
he had survived on the open prairie.

For him,
nothing broke the light of day.

From where I lay,
he was shadow lighted
by rising water mists.
Sky light was shining his body.

The animal in me crouched,
and waited for action.
Faintly I could see myself on his back,
like a ghost of living mystery.

In one leap I was one with it,
and we were galloping across the open prairie
followed by the herd.

I do not remember how my legs functioned,
but his loping grace
and wind-like swiftness
brought strength to my body.

In the healing medicine of being together,
we thought as one mind
and moved as one power.

We made our way,
from landmark to landmark,
measuring our days by the sun's journey.

His followers became my life,
as the strength of the mountains,
sky
and plains
moved us to Land-Of-The-Setting Sun.

Gold, round-leaf quaking aspen
waved us through The-Backbone-Mountains.

Red vine-maples called us through Cougar-Pass.
Red-orange dogwood trees and yellow tamarack,
high on the hillsides,
led us to the Gathering-Big-Waters.

In this high country,
Mountain Spirits roamed the land.
Forest animals came to watch us pass
on our journey.

The call of the mountains was in our ears.
The season tugged at our nostrils,
drawing us like a braided horsehair rope.

It was a difficult trail
to the Gathering-Of-Many-Waters,
but warm winds swept our path clean.

Clear streams followed weasel trails
beside yellow pines, spruce and fir,
giving us shade
and making the trail thick with life
under our hooves.

The mountains,
wind,
and, water,
were our medicine joy.
They gave us strength to walk the good earth.

Then one bright sun,
we crossed the Red-Bark-Madrone-Mountains,
and,
standing under tall cedars,
we saw The-Gathering-Of-Many-Waters
shining the day's face.

Tall trees and water waves
were alive with celebration.
We had followed the call of our hearts
and were ready to enjoy these life-waters.

When we reached the sand,
we ran through the coming-waves
and rolled in the setting sun,
as it sank over the outside waters.

Shell beads played under the waves.
Surf fish swam in the open water.
Along the shore,
giant trees brushed the sky.

Horse feed grew long,
in scattered meadow-pastures among the trees.

We played in the water ripples.
I swam in the great lagoon,
whose way to the Outer-Waters was deep
and swallowed the tall shore waves.

NADA

Sea lions peeked over long nose bristles.
Otters played in the seaweed.
Shark fins cut the water in long lines.
Octopus swished in and out among the rocks.
Jelly fish echoed their movement.
Shell fish hugged the shore rocks.
Water birds ran and sand danced.
Gulls flapped the air with many wings.

Each day's magic
caught me in its sleep light
and wrapped me in its blanket.

I asked the secrets of each sunset,
then fell asleep waiting for its vision.

During The-Moon-Of-The-Changing-Season,
my question-answer came.

XIV

BLACK-FACE-WHALE-TRIBE

A moving star went sky grazing;
which was a bad omen.

Then change winds,
which were fighting like wild animals,
blew in heavy clouds with big rain.

Lightning whipped the air.
Thunder rode close on every side.
Thunder-Chief's hail made our herd uneasy.

It was shouting,
all around:
"Hey-hey!
Hey-hey!"

We moved from the edge-water,
to get away from the wind talons
which tore the earth.

Wave-foam blew far above the tall trees.
As fog-dust whirled everywhere,
the wind told some of the forest
to lie down.

Our only protection was a rock overhang
on the nearby mountain side.

After three sleeps,
Sun rose dim,
and earth shook its skin in the rain.
We ran from our cave
and into an open meadow.
Earth continued shaking.

It was like land and sky were in a wrestling match.

In The-Land-Where-White-Giants-Live,
We could see a White-Watcher-Mountain smoking,
from fires inside her lodge.
Fire-Spirits ran down her edge.

Sky and dry land became grey.
Dust-ashes fell toward the rising sun.
When they shut out the sky,
Chief became restless.

Together we settled the herd,
so I could become the sentinel,
and find out what was happening.
As the hidden sun climbed the black sky,
I ran to the water.

The taste of salt was hanging in the air.
My eyes could not see the horizon.

Wolves had called a Black-Face-Whale-Tribe
into the lagoon.

They were holding council;
the wolves echoing the whale's calls.
Their voices mixing together,
made them one Tribe on land-water.

The whales could still hear the earth rattle,
and knew the big dance was not over.

I stood still,
saying to my heart,
"listen carefully."
For they had been in the Outer-Waters
when the mountain stood close by
and caught fire.

Everything was listening hard to hear.
Mother-Whale was the only calm voice in the Tribe.

   "Please my children."
   She said.

Then she stopped,
for what seemed like a long night waiting for the day.
　　"Great-Mother is simply breathing
　　a cleansing blanket over the earth.
　　She wants to shift a bit
　　and pull herself together.

　　She is going through a change.
　　As guardians of Holy-Presence,
　　we must celebrate the care she takes
　　to shift both air and land.

　　Her life is our song
　　and our joy is her comfort.
　　She emerged from our waters
　　and is herself the medicine power of All-Life.

　　In her cleansing, we are blessed.
　　Her medicine ashes bring richness to our waters.
　　Our food is her care.
　　Mother shows mercy to her children.
　　She does us well."

Whale-Tribe filled the lagoon with loud singing.
The voice of many tones
brushed the grass and forest trees.
Birds began to chirp again,
and insects started humming.
Even Wood-Pounding-Bird began tree drumming.

"Listen carefully..."
Mother-Whale began.
Then she coughed.
Something was wrong with her voice.
She was in the lagoon middle,
but I went to her very fast.

When I got there,
her Tribe was swimming around.
She was on her side,
almost dead.

I jumped on her floating body.
Life shined in her eye.

I lay my head beside her nose to listen.
Then I saw that it was filled with a long sea snake.
It was stuck there
by shellfish hanging on to her hide.

I kicked them off
and pulled on the snake
until it came out of her breathing place.

I was splashed with spray
and her huge body sank into the water.

Now I was in big danger.

Her Tribe thought
I had made her near death.
Just as their tails came to slap me,
she lifted me out of the water on her back.

"Easy my children."
She said clearly.
"The boy saved my life."

There was another big song,
while the whales jump-danced.

Then the water shook-trembled,
as the land had done.

The power pushed us into the sky
higher and higher,
up and down,
and up again.
Water rose above the shore.

Had Mother-Whale not been there,
I would have died from the earth-shake-washback.

She could have dived,
as she commanded her Tribe to do.
But she held me gently on top of the fast-changing water.

Her body took a great inside push.
When the others came to the top waters,
they moved near to her.

I could not see any injuries
but I heard what she said to the Tribe:
    "It is safe now.
    Go to the warm waters
    where our new ones will be born.

    Be content with the light of many days.
    Follow your new Chief with courage.
    You will do well
    I am with you.

    Live in power."

As the great animals circled,
quietly remembering the mysteries she had taught them,
light beams hung four sundogs in the sky.

The only one of the Tribe who stayed
was a small white whale,
who was to see her to daylight's ending.

    "No."
    She said.
    "The boy will stay with me
    till my completed rest.
    Go.
    Be healing medicine for the Tribe."

Mother-Whale and I were alone in the lagoon.
Debris from the tide-wave was everywhere.

NADA

"My son."
She began.
"We gave each other our lives.

Now I give you my death.

In it you will birth my power,
as Chief-Of-Chiefs.
You will understand what it means
to be 'Guardian-Of-Holy-Presence.'

Water is sacred to Earth-Mother.
It is the settling basin for sky dust
and the birth place of life.

Spirit-Presence is shadowed by it,
for it makes our holy parents knowable.

Earth-Mother wears water,
much as air wears light.
Air and water are the same,
just as are earth and light.

Do not be fooled by sky light or earth water,
for darkness covers 'the emptiness.'

Watch the empty darkness.
Spirit's lodge is in this silent unknown,
beyond words
or the thoughts of your eyes.

Great-Mystery cannot be known.

FACE-OF-THE-RISING-SUN

Even the shadows are only whispers
of The-One-Who-Cannot-Be-Grasped.

"We are those living shadows.
We must forget everything we know,
and let go of everything we are.

In the heart,
there are no dreams or thoughts,
only nothing.

With our hearts,
we get through light,
(the same as plants do
when they draw light into themselves)
and past water,
(the way frogs and salmon flies do
when they marsh hatch),
and past land or sky,
(the way our stars have done).

We become part of All.

Then we step past everything with silent feet,
just as sunlight passes through the water.

With respect,
we receive the gentle passing;
the same as we are now receiving my going shadow."

NADA

There was long silence.
All was quiet in the lagoon,
except for the water,
licking Chief's body,
and the gulls waving overhead.

Great-Presence was here;
hovering
like a Blue-Heron about to land.

Chief was being shown our journey trail.
   "Step my son,
   into emptiness,
   as you would into an unknown tide-pool.
   Give yourself to it.
   It will take care of you.

   On moonless nights
   when you cannot see,
   you must trust your way.

   You can trust emptiness.

   Step gently,
   for Great-Void is our guide.
   She is our way.
   She stands behind life.
   Emptiness calls us.
   She guides our journey.
   Trust Her with courage.

   Risk Her way."

There was another big silence.

We seemed to step from a cliff
into passing wind clouds.

> *"Let go my son,*
> *just as you sigh when Spirit-full.*
>
> *Breath out.*
>
> *Blow your breath to the wind.*
>
> *Trust her as eagles do.*
> *Ride their pathways.*
> *Let your heart fly you.*
>
> *Freedom calls,*
> *as a light beam calls the sun.*
>
> *Trust your heart.*
>
> *Emptiness calls,*
> *as an open sky.*
>
> *Feel her medicine inside.*
> *Depend on her for every action.*
> *Become the joy of her faithful friendship."*

Our next silence hung like stagnate air.

NADA

Sun was setting on a dark sky.
Blood red clouds reflected deep in the water.
In the Great-Water's pulse beat,
Chief and I washed gently toward shore.

> *"Release*
> *the easy hold on your body.*
>
> *Become*
> *a floating thought.*
> *Be too big for life power.*
>
> *Move,*
> *as a song through your throat,*
> *until you become the vision you sing.*
>
> *Disappear,*
> *as washing water on shore sand.*
> *Be absorbed.*
>
> *Let your presence fade,*
> *as bird songs upon the air.*
>
> *Give emptiness everything.*
>
> *Hide behind the wind."*

In our next silence,
we drifted
in the unending rocking of our Mother's care.
Chief's body moved
as gently in the water currents,
as earth moves among the stars.

Finally,
I heard her whisper:
  "We are together my son.

  Let The-Limitless-One move through you,
  until we drift,
  as wind clouds.

  We are star-oneness."

The merger of life-death was no clear line;
but the closeness of a breath,
which moved quietly over us.

A song washed to her in the breeze,
gently as day follows night:
          "Oh, Noble-One,
          we have waited long
          for the honor of your visit.
          You are home at last!"

We lay on the water-face like floatwood.

Seals began eating our underside-
sacred food for a hungry Tribe.
The washing tide,
rippling off the beach,
and the sharing of our body with the seals,
grounded us;
spilling me onto the wave-lapped sand.

Our sacred bond
felt like salt itching my skin.

Washed in Earth-Mother's life,
I felt her softness,
as the sand upon her shore,
a gentle sprinkle,
like eagle's down.

Blackface had showed me the change-way
and I lay on the sand
until the tide-moon lifted me,
as a praise-gift.

CHIEF-STALLION

This blessing brought a new sense of who I was.
As I looked about in the pale moonlight,
I realized the big wave
and the wind-waters
had put everything in a new place.

The rock outcropping high in the woods,
where the horses and I had gone for shelter,
were all I recognized in the dim light.

I wondered if Chief-Stallion and the herd were alive.
I could not sense his presence.

At dawn,
before the ravens left their perch,
I purified myself in the lagoon
and pushed through the ground-shore mess;
climbing the steepest area
to get away from the drift-log piles.

At last,
I reached the high-water mark.

NADA

It was the same level as our shelter-rock.
Trees had made crisscross basket patterns
and woven many snares.

Moving around the cave rock,
I found fallen trees blocking our shelter.
By the smell
I knew some of our band had been rubbed out,
and were headed for the silent shores.

Working my way through the log pile,
I heard some of them inside the cave.
I found a fallen cotton wood
and smeared sap on my hands and body
to quiet the horses.

I knew this was going to be a big task,
so, I sent my voice toward where the sun sets
to call on Spirit:
    "Hey-a-a-hey!
    Hey-a-a-hey!
    Hey-a-a-hey!
    Hey-a-a-hey!"

I could not feel Chief's presence,
So, he was either some other place or balancing his life.

I blew air though my lips in a low nicker,
which had become my comfort-song to him.
He answered.
I knew he was down and waiting.

Near the back rock,
two brood mares were in a crazy-frenzy.
Under a fallen tree,

three colts and several horses lay dead.

Two or three others were down
for no reason that I could see.

Where was Chief?
I called again.

He neighed from an upper part of the cave,
where he had been serving as sentinel.

Getting to him
I saw a clear uphill passage,
out of the fallen-down timber.

A large branch was ground holding him.
Even as I separated the limbs from the tree,
there was no room for him to stand up.
A large forked limb came across his shoulders.

From under him,
I removed some large rocks
which made him more comfortable.
Once the branch was gone,
it would give him better footing.

NADA

One limb fork finally broke.
The point gashed his shoulder.
He rolled sideways,
onto his back,
and into the ditch created by my rock rolling.
The holding limb hit the ground with a thump
and allowed him to roll onto his feet.

He was free,
but had an unsteady walk.

I left him standing,
and went to the others.

I cleared branches and pulled out stones,
to make an open pathway to Chief.

It was very long
before I got the two mares up to him.
His whinnying got them there,
for they were stubborn with fear.

I pulled at him so he would walk.
He hobbled.
At least he was moving!

Finally,
the three of them made it to water
in the close-by meadow.

One at a time
I got three others walking inside the cave.
It was difficult,
for they wanted to stand still.

They were bloat-puffed
and their eyes were over filmed.
I knew they would not live
unless I could get them out and walking.

They had seen the two mares go up the passage
and whinnied to them in the pasture.
So,
one at a time,
they stumbled up the steep pathway.

I could not tell if they really wanted to live.

All night I took turns walk-pushing them.
By morning two of them kicked at me
for bothering them.

I knew they would survive.

I had to leave the other mare to Chief,
he actually improved his hind quarters walking her.
I went back to the cave to find who was left.

At the lower end,
I found a small colt near its dead mother,
So, I half carried,
half pushed him out.
One of the mares was willing to nurse him.

Only seven horses from our band made it out,
and one was not alive for sure.
Most of our herd
had been washed into the flood trees.

It was not easy to stay where
so much buzzard meat was all around.
But we needed to pull ourselves together.
Chief hobbled around for many sleeps.

It was a good omen that we survived.

During The-Moon-Of-Falling-Leaves,
when geese and cranes flew to Land-Of-The-Bright-Sun,
The-People-Tribe returned to a plain
near where we now stood.

My life had become part of All-Life.

I no longer had a sense of being myself alone.

My people were the deer and wolves,
the coyotes and cougars,
the horses,
along with people.

I was one with stallion and whale,
with bear and snake,
with cedar and buffalo,
with eagle and coyote,
with wolf and prairie dogs.

But I was happy
as Stallion and I decided
to be among The-People-Tribe
during The-Season-Of-The-Bite-Wind.

I told him that their fire
would guide us to the meeting place.

We walked through Whistling-Elk-Pass,
separating our grass plain from the Big-Waters.
At the same time,
People-Tribe came for a solemn gathering
in Acorn-Meadows-Where-Elk-Feed.

They built their Council-fire,
and as night grew,
their sweet-smoke was rising
to The-Great-Change-Maker.

People Chief had just sent her voice,
calling the directions to stand together
with her people,
toward sky for wisdom,
toward the earth for food,
toward the sunset for gentle wind,
toward the Bite-Wind for easy cold,
toward the sunrise for good rain,
toward Land-Of-The-Sun for pleasant heat,
toward the stars for their presence at the Council.

Now they were in empty silence.
Waiting.

It fits the rhythm of nature,
a Council Meeting is half talk and half silence.

Silence pulls everything together.
It is the language understood by all.
It is a way to heart listen
to the voice of every Council which has ever met.

It was in this silence
that Stallion and I gave ourselves,
and what was left of our band,
to The-People-Council.

With deep thought
the ponies were distributed.

Power-Man and Chief selected both Stallion and me
for Chief's son.
The bond between us was strong
and the power of our friendship was deep.

Never had I felt such peace.

That sleep,
Father-Sun rode along the mountain ridge like a Chief,
in a red colored blanket,
with bright plumes waving far up in the sky.

Not more than a moon-change later,
when the shadows were long
and sunlight was falling heavy on the land,
several young men were out riding
on a hunting trip.

Stallion and I slipped from the ridge trail
overlooking the lake and tall forest.

Chief's son was badly hurt from the fall.
Stallion and I gave our life to him,
and put our skin around him
so medicine power could be strong
and our friendship kept alive.

PART II
LODGE-STORIES

I

POWER-MAN

When I woke-up from my dream-journey,
I felt like there was a big gap in my life.

Old-Man and I were beside the sacred fire.

Bite-smoke of
sage,
huckleberry
and dried sweet grass,
hung in the air.

I had a vision that the grass clumps,
out beside the pond,
were dancing in the dim light;
jumping up and down in their own reflection.
They were singing:
 "Ah-ho-ho-ho!
 Ah-ho-ho-ho!
 Ah-ho-ho-ho!
 Ah-ho-ho-ho!"

NADA

The sound was carried on the air
and out into the nearby meadows
by two flocks of white swans.

Even though my heart was smiling,
I wondered how anyone would understand,
for the vision-dream was mine and not theirs.

Power-Man felt my presence and said:
　　"I know my brother.
　　Save your vision.

　　Its meaning is wise and good.

　　Maker-Guardian has selected you
　　to teach The-Sacred-Trust
　　and to guard our people's Spirit-Power.

　　You must act on your vision,
　　so that the Powers are pleased.

　　You must guide our people.
　　Yours and my journey through great-smoke-dust,
　　is the same.

　　Having bunted our heads with our fears,
　　we have no threats to our strength.

　　This is medicine power.
　　Your lodge is now with our Ancestors.

You may not understand your power-vision now,
but act on whatever you know.

Do not talk of it.

Your life will tell your vision.
Your action is its power.

You are holder of Sky-Mystery,
and know how to walk the Story-Trail."

"Stories."
I whispered aloud.
"Mysteries of Spirit.
Lessons of nature.
Here we become Life Itself."

He nodded and said:
   "Each night
sleep-magic washes over everything.
It is a trail by which Life came to us:
a pathway leading all things together.

It keeps our thinking from setting snares
which capture our images.
Darkness erases everything that can be seen,
and frees us to be empty
of what the day would have us believe.

Dreams and stories are Freedom-Makers way
to help us understand.

They let our imagination explore the magic trails.
Our inside voices lead us
to what we do not know.

We follow our inside guides along the path.

Fear is the only thing
which keeps us from exploring".

"You are to hold your place in the medicine circle,"
was his reply to my unasked question.
"As Great-Mystery grows you,
people will come for wisdom.

Remember,
no story is what it seems.

What your voice says beyond the words
is the hidden power for each one who hears.

It is based on their experiences.
Its power is in their understanding,
for it draws from their own wisdom.

Through its images,
the story becomes theirs.
They create their own lessons."

Taking sacred bread,
stone-crushed from the red-topped amaranth,
he gave it to me,
saying:

"Holy food for a Shaman.
Eat Spirit.
We share its sacred power."

He gave me an eagle feather,
to mark my journey.
As he put it in my hair,
he said that my courage was an example for All.

I asked for his counsel.
He said,
after silently looking long
on the tall pond grass:
"Be self faithful.
Change not your thoughts for anyone.

-- Be Spirit
-- Never mind think.
-- Avoid looking with critical eyes.
-- Never be in charge."

He gave me a cycle of the seasons,
in which to learn his medicine discipline.

To do this,
his Spirit entered my body
and sat over my kidneys.

Then, he stroke-painted a red sun on my forehead.
The circle was for Great-Spirit.
The sun rays were the power directions.
The dot in the center was for my inside direction

and the declaration of my friendship with Spirit.

When Chief came into the lodge
She looked at me through joy tears,
and said:
    "My son,
    you have come back!"

    "Indeed, mother.
    I have returned as a Power-Man.
    I am like a log on which to cross a big stream."

    "Tell me,
    then,
    what to do
    with the furled feathers of Chief-Eagle-Claw,
    who says we have broken our agreements
    about land and hunting territory.
    He says he will have other Tribes join against us."

I offered her some willow-twig tea,
knowing that its strength to bend without breaking
would enter her mind as flexible-understanding.

    "Open your heart."
I said.
    "Chief-Eagle-Claw speaks like a blowing wind,
    when nothing comes of it.
    Hear this story."

II.

SHREWD-COYOTE

"Chief-Eagle-Claw is like Shrewd Coyote.

One day Coyote was out hunting for prairie dogs.
But none of them agreed to give him
their life strength.

Because he thought more of himself
than was his to claim in prairie ways,
he grew unhappy with his lack of prairie dog food.

He thought to himself:
'I'll show these critters who is who.'
Coyote was wily,
and wanted others to settle his unhappiness.
So, he tried to grab power.

That night,
when moon rose just above the ridge pines,
he howled for a coyote council.
He asked them to help him destroy The-Prairie-Dog-Tribe.

But the coyote clan did not like his idea
and would not support his swell-chested ways.

They asked long-tail magpie
to warn the prairie dogs,
to take a journey
on the day before his planned slaughter.

Slaughter-morning came
and the coyotes met on briar-patch-hill.

They looked like they were waiting for the sun
to tease some dogs from their peep holes,
but their tails were dragging with indifference.

Exactly when he said,
Wily came trotting by,
staggering under his own big-head.
His gooseberry colored eyes
gleamed under his raised eye brows and upper lids.

   'Whiff, Whiff,'
   his nose went in the air,
with a snooty, *'I-don't-care-for-prairie-dogs'* attitude.

He stopped long enough to say:
   'From where the sun now stands,
   by night fall
   all the village dogs
   will be dead!'

As they started off for peep-hole-village,
the other coyotes grinned
and hung out their tongues to slobber.
When they arrived at the village,
all agreed to scatter,
but said that no one would touch a prairie dog
until Wily had killed the first one.

   'Sniff, sniff,'
  puff-nosed Wily went,
thinking:
'this will be easy!'

One coyote,
in a shriek little voice,
squeaked a prairie dog noise.

Off Wily ran,
high bush-tail waving back and forth in delight.

On the far side, another coyote squeaked;
then one in the center.

All day Wily ran,
seeking his revenge,
while coyotes sat and prairie dog squeaked.

Eagles and hawks gathered overhead
and filled the sky with laughter.
Even the foxes and field cats came to watch.
Snakes,
who love prairie dog meat,
crawled over to see Wily run about.

At sundown,
Wily was foaming at the mouth,
and puffing on the air,
from lack of water.

He realized that in his revenge attempt,
he had been a fool.
His trick had landed on his own head.

Had he killed all the prairie dogs,
his food supply would have been gone.

Magpie,
who came along to see about things,
saw Wily headed up Rocky-Butte,
his tail tucked between his legs.

  'Balance,'
  called magpie,
  'Humble balance is life's secret.'

So,
My Chief,
Eagle-Claw and Coyote help you know your
power boundaries
and your care wisdom."

She laughed,
as she handed me the empty tea cup.
In her laugh,
she let Chief-Eagle-Claw fly from her mind.

Her delight also set the next council meeting.

Just after she left the Sacred Lodge,
she called the Tribal Council together,
to tell them of my return.

They painted me red
and I sat down among them.
We took council about the uncertain weather
and the survival of our Tribe.

The White-Watcher-Mountain was spreading
its dust blanket
over the valley floor.
They asked for wisdom
and wanted me to call the dark cloud clothes
from the sky.

Rather than send my breath to blow the clouds,
I shared a laugh-story:
"Two dandelion plumes
were floating across the valley
on winds created by tall white-blossom clouds.
As lightning tore the sky
and thunder rattled against the mountains,
one plume said to the other,
'Who knows how we shall survive
through this dangerous storm?'"

Many Elders did not find this funny,
even though I and others laughed.
It made some not-happy
that this was all I had to say or do.
They saw me as, 'no-good.'

Those who understood their own wisdom,
that they must blow their cares away,
stopped their survival concern.

III

WHO SIRES THE BUFFALO?

Not too long after my first Council Meeting,
a big bully came seeking advice.

We had known one another since childhood,
but shame covered him
like a water drenching storm.

He looked only where his feet stepped.
Since he was smothered with shame,
he waited long
to talk about his visit.

I finally said:
  *"It is not because you came for silence
  that you are here."*

He then said that none of the women
with whom he had shared his breeding stick
during the Bite-Wind-Dance,
had made children for the Tribe.

The other men teased him,
saying that his best muscle only flapped
in the wind made by his bragging.

As I listened quietly,
Old-Man guided me to walk around him
with my hands held toward his body.
After a long pause,
while I listened to Old-Man,
we went for sweat lodge purification.

We entered the buffalo skin lodge
and spread cleansing sage on the floor
and sweet sage on the hot stones.
When our breath was almost gone,
from the strong heat and sage smoke,
we came out to swim in the pond.

After we whip-dried ourselves with sage branches,
we smeared mud over our bodies
and chanted:
   "Put the earth on me.
   Put the land on my body."

Then we sat in the center circle
of the Medicine Teepee.
His breeding basket rested
on the soft, healing earth.

He needed her strength.

FACE-OF-THE-RISING-SUN

I danced around him,
using a buffalo siring the basket rattle
and fanned him with the cleansing wind
from a pheasant wing.

Once earth power began rising in his body
I threw cold water over him.
This called for his healing power deep inside.

Then I sat beside him and said:
  "My brother,
  in buffalo traditions,
  the one who least knows his strength
  is chosen to sire the cows.

  It helps him stand strong --
  something men get only from women.
  Men who know their power,
  sex-play among themselves.

  Any who cannot enjoy this,
  must find their woman-strength.

  Accepting this power,
  allows your breeding rocks to drop.
  Only then is everything ready.

  Making children does not come from striving.
  Fertility power
  comes from quiet resting in yourself."

These were not easy words for him to hear,
so, I told him a story:
  "When a small black calf
  was born in Buffalo-Tribe,
  the male eyebrows raised.
  He was so scrawny
  they agreed that he was born
  as wolf-feed.

  The other calves smiled
  at his wobbly stand and knobby knees.
  His run was a big laugh for them all.
  His father was ashamed of his skinny son.
  But mother's milk was fattening.

  So,
  by the time he turned yellow,
  he had strong muscles.

  His body was well put together.
  The only problem was
  that he carried the laughter of his calf days
  in his ears.
  He heard only their fun-making voices.

  His body grew strong.
  His push was very big.
  Wolves were afraid of his huge head.

  Everyone in the Tribe
  now raised their eyebrows in respect.

But he pulled their laughter through his unhappiness,
and made his way in life
with force, instead of fun.

With his power held against himself,
he did not know his own strength.

He pushed the other bulls around.
With great fight,
he made his way with the cows.
He was too pushy-
a bad omen for strength-balance.
So, Buffalo Council met him head to head.
They put him in charge of cow siring.

In this role,
his unsureness was so strong
that he became too protective of the herd
and would not allow other creatures to visit.

It took five breeding seasons
before he learned from the cows
the balance of being gentle.

Once he grew deaf
to the laughter of his childhood,
his offspring increased,
and a dignity,
due his great body,
began to happen.

NADA

Accepting himself
brought power-strength.
He no longer looked under his eyes
to hurt others.

He had learned
his own sacred wonder,
and the joy of being at home with himself.

He no longer told others what to do.
They volunteered to do everything."

We closed our session with my saying:
"My brother,
may the Spirit of Great-Buffalo
be good medicine to you."

To help him feel his manhood strength,
I gave him special foods to eat.
He was to eat the spleen, pancreas and kidneys
of a male rabbit or buffalo
and to drink tea made from the buds and branch tips
of cedar, hemlock and fir,
for at least one meal each new moon.

During the Season-Of-Growing-Things,
I had gathered the light green tips from trees
high in the mountains
where medicine power was strong.

After eating this diet,
he was able to discover his inside-peace,
and began siring many children
for our Tribe.

GENTLE-WATERS and WARBLER-HAWK

A mother brought the lifeless form of her child to my lodge.
I did not know how to use the many medicines
hanging on the teepee poles.
But Power-Man helped me.

From the palm of my open hand,
I blew smoke in all the directions.
Then I sent my voice,
as an offering to Spirit;
a way by which power could step into my mind
and tell me what to do.

I chanted into ecstasy,
and carefully listened.
I was told how to brew
chokecherry twigs and pine nuts into tea.

While letting it cool-settle,
I danced around the child's body;
purify her with smoke from sweetgrass braids
and cedar boughs.

As I danced,
I felt power coming into my feet
and crawling up my legs like ants.
A great crowd of spirits came into the Sacred Lodge.
They filled the little girl with life.

Outside the rain was ground dancing.
The crows were shouting at each other.
When earth-power grew up to my heart,

I knew all would be well for the girl.
When she sat up and drank the tea.

I chanted her sound
to Medicine-Spirit and Earth-Mother.
Then I wrapped her in wolverine skin,
so that its spirit would enter her body.
When she began to sweat,
I knew the cure would hold.

I sent my voice to the sky:
    "Hey-a-a-hey!
    Hey-a-a-hey!
    Hey-a-a-hey!
    Hey-a-a-hey!"

In one sleep she was well,
even though she was very tired.

When she awoke,
I told her a life-walk story.
    "One day Gentle-Waters
    (as squirrel mother called her daughter)
    was running along some skinny branches
    near their nest,
    when Gray-Hawk saw her.
    Mother alarm-chattered,
    which made Gentle-Waters rush to their lodge,
    more scared than ever before.

    She grew her fear so big
    that she did not want to leave the nest.

    Her fear even got bigger than her desire to live.

    One day a little warbler bird came
    and sat beside the nest.
    It sang a happy song,
    which happened like this:

    'Let your heart not wither.
    Let your heart not wither.'

    It made Gentle-Waters forget her fears
    and she began to dance the freedom song.
    Jump-hopping from limb to limb,
    Gentle-Waters found herself in the meadow sunshine.
    (Hop, Hop, Hop.)

    She ran freely in the light.

As her joy grew,
so did her adventure-courage.

Then one day,
when the dry voice of blowing-leaves was singing,
Grey-Hawk swooped down and grabbed her.
In the middle of a jump over warbler bird,
Gentle-Waters became a meal for baby hawk.

If you listen very carefully
to the end of a hawk's call,
it makes a little squirrel squawk."

She liked the story
because she had heard the little squawk
as her last breath
and was happy to breath freely again.

It was a new life for her.

She knew that she had given her life to All-Life,
and her body was renewed because of her surrender.

Because of her healing,
I became known as a Life-Maker.

V

CROW-BEAR'S STRUGGLE

I watched one of our Mother's-Children,
as he struggled with his rising powers
of becoming a man.

Each moon he grew two fingers nearer the sky.
He struggled with his growing body;
stumbling over his moccasins
and trying to use his taller and taller legs.

He was so mean
that the other children did not play with him.
He pushed his strength everywhere;
hurting people and injuring animals.

He was growing like a crooked stick;
a wild briar
who had to remain a Mother's-Child
until his initiation into our Tribe.

FACE-OF-THE-RISING-SUN

As a Mother's-Child,
everything was allowed
and he simply grew wild in the meadows.

One night his mother brought him to my lodge
with burns all over his body.
He had fallen into the camp fire,
because he went against her voice.

She had pulled him out of the flames
and thrown him into the cold river water,
so that the fire in his body
would not cook his muscles.

After I pulled his burn-hide loose
I covered him with smashed cactus plant
and bear grease.

Then I began drumming and calling Spirit.
It was long before I could feel the boy's power.

I prayed:
> *"Great Spirit.*
> *Grandfather.*
> *You are the only one.*
> *You made everything*
> *including us.*

You are the life-source;
the growing mystery.
You made us to be in strong health.
Your power can make our health over,
just as the plants grow.

You have provided herbs
to help us walk well.
As it is now on this boy,
he shall have strength to be made well.
To you I send my voice."

I tried to find a medicine song
which fit his pain-endurance.
It was soothing quiet
and wove its pattern;
bonding us together for healing.

As his body drank the cactus juices,
he asked for a story.

This is the one I told:
  "As baby crow
  was scratching his beak side-ways,
  looking for food,
  he decided he did not like
  being an ugly black critter,
  who had to hop about eating leftover garbage.

So, he said to his mother:
    'I want to be a bear.
    If I have to be black
    and grub around for food,
    I want to be strong-powerful.
    I want to be big,
    so others will give me what I want.'

Magpie overheard his talk,
and said:
    'I will condemn you
    to whatever you want to be.'

With the flick of her long tail
she made baby crow into a big,
clumsy bear.

He waddled about knocking into things
and tore up big logs
to find grubs and termites.
He went to the river
where he splashed fish from the water
and ate them.

For baby crow,
it was a bad life.
Because,
more than anything,
he missed being able to fly.

As a fat, earth-stuck bear,
he had no freedom.

As the sleeps went by,
he felt more and more squashed by his body.
The way for bears
was very different than the way for crows.

He didn't like how the earth pulled at his feet.
He got very tired
trying to move through ground air.
He couldn't even hop;
and standing on two legs made him almost dizzy.

He just never felt natural.

He begged magpie to give back his before life.
She agreed to do only half of what he wanted.
He could have a crow's body and a bear's mind
or he could have a bear's body with a crow's mind.

He chose to have a crow's mind
and became a Bear-Tribe inventor.

He knew about air flight
and used his body weight
to figure out how to get beyond many bear limits.

He got round rocks and straight tree limbs
to help move heavy objects.
He invented the hunting stick,
with its rawhide string,
and arrows for flight in the air.

He was able to have fun
making his difficulties into everyday use".

We had a laugh about Bear,
and how black the boys body looked in two days.

After I took off the herbs,
his mother,
the boy
and I
chewed hemlock bark to put over the burns.

We then covered it with yellow cedar bark
to restore his outside skin
and leave no burn marks.

After his hurt was gone,
he lost the mischief which hurt others,
and the coyote look in his eyes.

He became good,
like the universe.

VI

RATTLESNAKE

For many, many, moons
Rattlesnake had stayed silently alone outside camp.

When he was a Mother's-Child,
he was playing, *'A-Bear-Chase-Me!'*
(a racing game)
beside the river with his friends.
One of them fell into the fast-waters and drowned.

The boy's mother
thought Rattlesnake had pushed her son into
the water.
So, she placed a snake curse on him.

This curse was woven like a spider's web
to kill a fly-bug.

People began making fun of him.
When they met him,
they would say,
"Pooh, Pooh,"
(in a thin high voice of a drowning person's ghost).

Some said he smelled like a snake,
and were afraid that they would be
poisoned by his touch.
Others said ghosts trailed him like fog.

Even though he was a stranger
to their false looks and actions,
fear of his curse blocked his path,
and put his life
in the way of things he could not avoid.

His fears came as glimmers in the night fire,
then went up with the flame
to join the darkness.

During the day,
these strange shapes
sometimes came back to trouble him;
making faces which moved in secret,
half seen in the shapes he knew
or dimly felt hiding nearby.

Sometimes his fear pounded his heart faster.
It was like a tight drum-skin,
beating out his thoughts.

He was extra afraid
of the stillness when everyone was sleeping.

NADA

Snared by his fears
and trapped by the silent aloneness,
his curse followed him
in darkness and in sunlight.

He felt pushed aside;
as if people looked at him
and pointed.

He walked like a stranger among us.
It is hard
to deal with the arrow heads
which point to one's openness to be shot.

Since he did not seem to belong to his people,
he wanted to be alone.

I was the only person in the Tribe he came to see.

One night his fears were so big
that they filled his vision.

He wanted his curse to end.

So, I called to Spirit
and found myself in a trance.
I began singing and dancing.

Birch bark rattles
which spoke the voice of Spirit,
and fawn hide,
stretched over a hollow oak drum,
allowed a healing Spirit
to be present in the rhythm.

Sage and huckleberry smoke created the air
in which to see Spirit's movement.
Mushrooms and sage tea
opened the paths connecting our bodies.

The spider's web was pulling together.

I made requests to The-Great-Powers
by drumming, chanting and singing.

I put together more than one song:
   "O Great-Father-Sun
   and Earth-Mother of our Ancestors,
   in our being together now,
   we open our hearts to health.

   Make us be in harmony.
   Pour light through us."
(I poured water over us both.)

   "Wash us with care.
   May we be as the water.
   May we live to be old
   and always be pure.

Cleanse us with your touch."
(I touched the red-hot stones,
then touched Rattlesnake.)
   "May our lives be strong,
   as these stones.

   Make your trail our pathway.
   Shine power out of us as the sun.
   Let our trail be the stars."
(We looked toward both Sun and Moon).

   "Healer-Spirit,
   make our journey like a river flow.
   Let our hearts bubble as a spring".
(Someone chanted a water bird song,
as we washed ourselves in water.)

   "Light our trail.
   Shine away the darkness.
   Blow hope into our lungs."
(I took a deep breath
and blew it into his spirit blanket.)
   "Be our guide when clouds cover the trail.

   Our eyes search and our ears wait.
   Open our vision.

   Let peace be our rest.
   Our hearts reach up,
   as the bite-curved moon."
(I danced a wind dance.)

"Unite us as rock."
(Together we lifted a heavy stone.)
   "Cover us with buckskins of beauty.
   Make come true what we ask."

It was three sleeps before he woke up.
Spirit was in his heart.
After his healing,
he saw that privacy-hiding made his fear.

It had guided him to distrust.
It made his courage weak
and his risk-confidence be without bravery.

He had been snared
by his own disrespect,
and hand given up his freedom.

He was feeding on his own unhappiness.
He was possessed
by what he hated in himself.

After his healing,
he found that love made him strong.

Rattlesnake continued to live outside the circle,
held tight by other's private curses of themselves.

He grew to understand
that they did not let anyone see
their secret fears;
which they put onto him.

The taboos which hunted them down in quiet darkness,
they pushed onto him;
until they became messed up,
believing he was the one who made their inside doubts.

But Rattlesnake did not give up his vision.
He refused to be destroyed by deceit.

This gave him freedom.

He found that he did not have to take serious
the names they called him.
He learned to laugh at the fears
with which they hurt themselves.

He walked without their gossip weight,
for he knew their fright was not his.

His courage,
in understanding their hidden fears,
gave him great power.

Through their fears,
he knew the limits each person set for themselves,
and the path they took inside,
to avoid their deep secrets.

Pushed aside by the Tribe,
he made friends with the animals.
He studied the ways of our animal Ancestors,
and they shared their secret powers with him.

Knowing the fears of his people
and the animal power secrets,
he began to carve totem animals
which represented each person's medicine.

At the start,
people were afraid of the carvings
which he put outside their teepees.

Soon they discovered
that this medicine power
brought them happiness-strength.
The totems became good omens for their lives.

They got courage to risk scary things,
even in the evening
when the growing shadows
became disturbing forms of returning spirits.

The people
never accepted Rattlesnake
for the great teacher he was.

He stayed outside camp all his life
and howled with the wolves.

No one,
to this very night,
knows whether it is the wolves
or Rattlesnake howling.

Can you tell your teacher from your fears?

PART III
THE OLD ONE'S STORIES

In the night silence,
Old-Man told me many stories of our Ancestors.
They are the traditions of our Ancient-Ones.
Sharing the next four stories
will help you understand all the others better.

STORY I

FIRE

One day Rising-Dawn-Mist was down by the river,
thinking about her biggest wish;
her desire to have a child.

She longed for one so much
that she never noticed
she was staring at Sun.

Communing with the Infinite Spirit,
she felt its heat,
and was blind to everything but its light.
Suddenly she felt a great heart leap,
bounding like a deer from the thickets.

It was Spirit magic,
and she opened herself to Sun
as to a man.
From their meeting,
she made a child.

She named him, "Fire."
He was Sun in a body.
His was sacred power.

Now that Rising-Dawn-Mist had her child,
she did not know what to do with him.
So, she sat down to drink some tea
made of juniper berry leaves.

The song of the swaying pines,
told her not to take him to her teepee.

Instead,
she went to the willows and reeds.
She said to them:
"You grow beside the waters.
You know and understand the river.
You bend to the needs of all.
I have come to take your life.
Forgive me for you are to be used
for my son's cradle-canoe."

The reeds forgave her,
and she wove a large canoe,
which she covered with tree pitch-rosin.

As she placed her son in the canoe,
and put it to float in the stream,
her heart pressed heavy against her chest.

His father's heat
built the boy's life-fire.

In the river's care,
the boy grew
But he had a deep thirst,
which the river waters could never stop.

It was his need to be his inside power.

One early dawn,
a beautiful girl,
from a village, far downstream from his mother,
came to bath.

She waded into the stream near some reeds,
and was surprised to find Fire's canoe.
Taking him to her heart,
she gave him food and love.
She named him, "Water-Sparkle."

He grew very fast
and could do many things.
He could do magic;
which the children were excited to see.

Because of his power,
many wanted to use him to fix their desires.

The hunters begged him to join them,
because he had the ability
to take and give life whenever he wanted.
They asked him to kill,
so, all could eat.

Those in arguments with others,
wanted him to destroy their enemies.
Others came to him,
that he would deal with their jealousy
and revenge desires.

He refused them all.

For power,
used to put one life over another,
was not his way.

He taught people
that everything they thought
would come true.

No matter what they wanted,
they could make it happen.
This was true
so long as they believed it would happen.

He said that good is always close by,
if it is accepted.

He taught us how to openly receive what we want.

Because of him,
we found that the fire power of our mind
is what made our lives.

CHANGE-BRINGER

One evening Power-Man and I were sitting together.

I was trying to understand what happened at death.

He told me of our beginnings.

It was about things
which reach to the start of all that is;
to a place before all memory.
Those were the days of the Old-Ones,
the beginners,
when life was young.

He said that before the world was made,
emptiness was everywhere.
Blackness covered everything.
In the birth cave of emptiness,
before the dawning,
came a thought from The-Great-Source.

Out of this thought,
water came to be.
The water was mother.
She was nothing.

Mother was empty,
just as she was.

Life flowed from her,
and became all that is.

Out of the empty blackness,
all things came to be.

This is the power of all that happens.
It is the growing power.

It is rooted in Night-Mystery,
as it reaches toward the light.

When animals
birds
and plants
came out of mother,
they were equal.

Every little thing was made for something.
Everything could speak with one language.
Plants shared in thoughts.
It was when magic and mystery were one.

Everyone decided to celebrate
their oneness in being alive.

In the wildness of their joy,
the Big-Waters began to stir and foam.
It looked like Mother was beating
a big froth with two fingers.
As the water-tide got higher and higher,
the waves were whipped into chaos.

From the wind,
made by all the water foam,
crow (who could fly at night and not be seen),
was nearly knocked from her spruce tree perch.

She was having a good dream
and did not want to wake up.

But the Star-Nation was holding council,
beside the bright sky trail,
so, she left her perch
to find out what was going on.

When she got over the bubbling water
she saw it was Big-Turtle coming up for air.
Its shell was like an island.
So, crow landed on it.
What a good thing she did!

At the twinkle of a star,
Change-Bringer blew up a storm,
and threw fire from the clouds.

Changer- Bringer was searching for all the creatures.
These supernatural beings had special powers.
He wanted to change them
before People-Tribe arrived.

Those able to swim strong
he made into whales and dolphins:
Guardians of the Great-Waters.

Wing-flappers,
who could fly with fastness,
became eagles and hawks.
They took over the upper sky,
as messengers of Great-Mystery.

Those who could run on long journeys,
became wolves and deer.
They lived on the dry land.

Frogs and snakes
took the under-world powers.
Things which were large and moved slowly,
were made into mountains or tall trees.

The extra strong
became bears or mountain sheep.
They ruled the mountains.

So, land, water and sky
became populated with Creature-Tribes,
who were stronger and more powerful
than the People-Tribe who came later.

When Sun left his lover,
in the under-earth,
and was wearing his shining clothes,
these Creature-Tribes put on their special robes.

This made it
so people could not see them as they were
and would not be afraid of them as monsters.

All creatures were changed into birds,
beasts,
fish,
rocks
and trees.

Change-Bringer always gave
the creatures what they wanted,
according to their nature.

Coyotes wanted to be clowns.
Salmon chose scales
and lived under the waters.

Alder and cedar chose bark
so they could be trees
and live in the woods.

Bear and otter chose fur.
Rainbow liked to flutter her clothes
so she got to play in the mist-cloud sky.

Worm became a great teacher.
He crawled into a white teepee
and turned himself into a butterfly.

This showed people how to change
from earth creatures into sky beings.

He showed everyone the courage to fly,
even when his wings were frail against the wind.

All these Old-Ones
knew people would come
to hunt and fish for them
or to chop them down.

But it was not their death.
They just returned to their villages
and came back
to help The-People-Tribe survive again and again.

The-People-Tribe could seek their power
and ask for The-Old-Ones to help.
They were people's extra power.

This is how our power animals
and sacred places came to be our help-mothers,
our life-force
and our power-source.

They match who we are.
When we sit quietly before them,
we change into our animal powers.
We have their power
until we become finished.

One day we will have learned their teachings enough
so that we can return from the waters
and our own source.

We will know this in Crow's yellow eye.
For that is the only thing
which lets you know where she flies in the night.

COYOTE'S HOT

Our Old-Ones enjoyed sex stories.
Sex-power was the only reason to be alive.

Here is one about Coyote:
One day,
Old-Coyote was out
slinking his way through the sage brush,
looking for critters to eat.

He pulled the earth with his front paws
and threw it all around the place,
like a gopher digging in easy dirt.
Suddenly he came upon a centipede
which stung his nose.

He yelped so loud Blue-Jay heard the cry
and flew faster than a wind-driven sand storm
to Coyote's rescue.

When she got there,
she found Coyote whimpering about,
as if it were his end life.

He didn't even chase a rabbit
near the chaparral patch.

So, Blue-Jay reminded Coyote
of his well developed siring rod,
and told him to use it at least one more time
before his death.

The thought so excited Coyote
that he hung it out
and went looking for anything he could find to enjoy.

Nothing seemed satisfying,
even though he tried a fallen tree,
a moss bank,
another male coyote,
who slinking off yapping,
    "Get off my tail!"

By this time, Coyote was so prepared for action
that he sat down to relieve himself.
He howled for all the forest critters
to come to the big event.

He expected them to
"ooh"
    and
"aah,"
but rabbit started laughing so hard
that he fell over backward.

This made Coyote as mad
as if dirt had been thrown in his face.
He tucked himself away
and started chasing rabbit.

All this frolic was so exciting to the critters
that they danced around a big pine tree
on the hill top.

In the middle of the dance
lightning hit the tree.
Its long leaves began to burn
and dropped like arrows from the sky.

Meanwhile,
Coyote was angry because his siring rod
was no longer the attention center.

He came running back up the ridge
to show off some more.
When he got to the pine tree
he lifted his leg to pee
and some of the burning arrows fell on his tail.

The smell of burning fur was awful.
But he was so sex hot,
he never noticed his tail was on fire.

Suddenly he began to really yelp!

He ran down the hillside,

through the briar patch,
along the ridge-top sage fields
and toward the river;
his wind almost out!

What great excitement:
Everyone was howling,
    "Ah-ooooo
    Ah-oooooo
    Ah-ooooooo!"

When Coyote jumped into the river,
the hair burned off his back side,
it looked like he had stripped off his furs for a race.

The whining voices of the soft brush
shouted their smiles.

The clouds were laughing so much
that they cried raindrops;
which put out the fire.

But even today,
the flame is in the wood.
If you don't believe it,
rub sticks together.
You will find that they catch fire and burn.

When this happens, we say:
    "Coyote is full of sex again."

THE SECRET OF COYOTE'S MAGIC

Once there were no edges
to land, water or air.

Everything alive moved easily between themselves.

They simply used their ability to change.
This magical power to change themselves
came from moon light.

This medicine-spirit was so strong
that all living things existed peacefully together.

They did not think of themselves
as different from one another.
Everything alive was one power.

One day,
around the Sun-Council-Fire,
Change-Bringer decided
to split up everything according to roles
and assigned customs
to the different living creatures.

Once everything had its place and action,
they made up laws.
According to their assignments,
birds flew,
fish swam,
animals walked,
air blew,
water washed waves
and land remained (fairly) solid.

They could no longer use medicine power
to change themselves as they wished,
unless, they were magicians.

To see that no one had this power,
darkness ate the moon.
After chewing it for a while
night spit the bits out into the sky.

These bits became our stars.
The space holes pulled them into circle trails.

So, Star-Nation became the source of all things.
Darkness remained empty,
according to its role,
and was itself,
a secret mystery.

All who saw light dust
sifting through sky darkness,
believed it was real.

This dust became the form of all things,
and people began to worship these things as sacred.
They even called themselves forms
and made themselves into things.

They didn't know,
but night was giving birth to day.
(It still creates each new day.)
From the darkness came day light.

Because night was when Spirits come very close,
the day made what the night revealed.
From death in the dark earth,
plants grew to the light.

Night held earth's growing power,
and made her strong.

In The-Cold-Season,
night held on longer,
so, Spirits came on top of the land to sleep.

In night rest,
all things were given life power.
Life was put in order by the moon.
She renewed everyone in sleep.

Power was in the darkness;
strength was in the light.

NADA

As long as people kept this straight,
they were guardians of the cycles.
But many got mixed up
and thought strength was power.

These people became violent
and out of step with nature.

For them,
darkness became offensive.
People began to be afraid of it.

They said that Darkness-Spirit
could not be trusted,
that it was the mean-presence
of death-destruction.

They said that if allowed to,
night would devour everything
just as it had chomped up the moon.

In the darkness
many lost themselves,
as in a dream.

Long after the reality had faded,
they remembered only an indefinite feeling.

To so totally lose one's face,
caused big concern.
Experience became too undependable.

It came to the place where,
only a very few went to live in darkness.

During daylight,
Sun lighted darkness into shadow,
but could never completely hide
all traces of this silent black power.

Some became afraid of their shadows,
believing them to be something of themselves
which they should avoid.

Owl and Wolf laughed at all this craziness,
so, their hooting and howling became death omens.

Mouse and rat also tried
to show that there was not night danger.
They got a name for being nuisances.

So, the world of day and night;
of light and dark;
got split apart.

The ones who believed light was best,
denied all shadows,
even inside themselves.

They began to worship Sun.

NADA

Those who lived in darkness became quiet and shy.
They enjoyed the night,
as a soft warm blanket,
and worshipped Moon.

Coyote decided not to listen to any of this craziness
and ran boldly in the trail,
no matter whether it was day or night.

He became so good at finding his way,
that he learned the secrets of both day and night.
None surpassed Coyote,
in wisdom and skill.
He has learned to live with All-Life.

This is the reason he is such a good magician.
He knows that the power within
cannot be forgotten,
even when it is asleep.

So, Coyote became the power balance of play;
of healing and laughter;
of tricks and benevolence.

PART IV
CEREMONIES

I.

CEREMONIES
OF SEASONS

Our life created the seasons.
Each one had its special activities.
Our ceremonies pulled life together,
like the laces on our shirts.

These celebrations
were the points around which our lives turned.

Our dances were our great joy;
simple dramas;
acting out Spirit's wordless possibilities.

Without them our traditions would be
forgotten-gone.

In a big circle,
we bent our knees and danced our hearts;
with drums pounding,
heads down
and bodies bent like an unstrung bow.

We wore beaded moccasins on our feet
and feathers in our hair
or down our back in a large sun,
powerfully stomping out our ancestors' rhythms

and wildly crying whoops of ecstasy.

We entered the mysterious flow of life,
singing with all our force.
    "Hi-Yah! Ai! Hi-yah!"
We mixed our tracks
according to the world-throb alive in us.

This made the earth work well.
Our songs were like a flock of cranes
rising from the marsh swamp,
called by The-Unseen.

We sang across the power forces
that made the world,
and ordered life to be.
We sang our impulses.

During the Season-Of-The-Death-Wind,
the Chief's and my central lodges
were as popular as our smoke lodge.

These were places for fire-light sharing,
song singing,
tale telling,
and eating our food supplies.

It was when we
    " wa-ha-ha-ed"
and
"ho-ho-ho-ed"
at life.

NADA

All this joined us together like a forest of trees.

Our festivals were celebrations of this bond.
The Festival-After-White-Feather-Crystals-Fall,
was always held during the Moon-Of-The-Cold-Wind.

It was the feast of unreality;
when magic became Freedom-mind in action.

Sometimes it was called The-Festival-Of-The-Women.

They prepared special foods,
which tasted like the mountains.

They also dressed in beautiful skins
or woven cedar bark.
Their shell beadwork
and bright colored clothes
made them especially desirable.
Their shells and the seed pods
on their skirts sang,
  'Shu-shu-shu...'

During this festival,
they slowly shuffled in earthbound softness,
as if wearing away the earth.

Our Chief was provided a new costume
and a head band of beads and feathers.
She passed out head bands for each of us.

212

After that,
cedar,
boiled in alder bark to make it red,
and pounded so it would fluff like mountain sheep wool,
was handed to everyone.

We used it to wipe our faces
and take away our outside appearance.
Then we painted ourselves with animal fat
which was mixed with dried red or black powder.

White Swan's down was put on our heads
to purify our thoughts.

Until the Season-of-Growing-Things,
we no longer lived by our usual names.
We were purified for our ancestral-animal names.

It was a sacred time for sharing gifts
and offering praise to one another.

It was also a time to remember our Ancestors.
We held ceremonies,
calling them back to celebrate with us.
Whether we called them back,
or not,
we thought of our Old-Ones.

It was how we remembered
that we all are alive
and we all are dead,
in our unending mystery journey.

All these festivities
were designed around appreciation
and reverence for those we loved.

Because this was the season
when The-Spirit-Moving-All-Things is powerful,
we usually brought new dancers and singers
into the ancestral line.

When the Great-One selected a dancer/singer
that person was put into a quiet place alone,
and attended by those who became their physical guardians
through a difficult initiation.

Until the dancer/singer received their dance/song,
they were isolated from every day walk-about.

Their initiation dance-journey,
on our naked Mother,
was a walk around Spirit's world.

It was part of Mother's dream.
This was a very private journey
from which each person returned all different.

Never would they be the same.
  "Aii-Ya!"

It was just like the worm
which pulls itself from its teepee,
as a butterfly.
It is a time of death and birth.

When Spirit gifts arrived
the person was purified with water and paint.
The floor was cleansed with duck down,
so that the feet which dance on purified ground
would be blessed.

The song/dance traveled from Spirit
and was our special experience
of The-Great-One.

We simply took each breath as it came,
and then gave it back to The-Great-One
with deep body sighs of ecstasy,
  "Huh-Huh!"

This was no ordinary wind puffing,
but a wordless mystery of Spirit-Wind sound.
It came from deep in our bodies
as a release of fire-power.

With it came medicine power harmony.
This was the rhythm of our dance.
It became our living prayer,
even in the death sleep.

Sometimes this was a hungry season,
and we did not have fresh food supplies.

We survived on powdered camas bulbs
which made flour for flat bread,
acorn mush,
our most basic food,
along with dried fish, fruit and meat.

When our hunters brought back game to share,
or our fishermen brought a new supply
of shell food or fish,
these were times of joyful celebration.

Someone would sing in a long voice
    "Hi-i-i-i-i-i-i-I,"
and the people would respond:
    "Hi-i-i-I, hi-hi-hi-hi."

A medicine prayer-song for this season was:
    "Great-Power,
    make our people happy.
    Have pity on any of us
    who are in want or need.
    Help us to live long-health."

II.

THE-SEASON-OF-GROWING-THINGS

In The-Season-Of-Growing-Things,
our festivals were times of letting go
with wild abandon.

After sleeping under her blanket,
Mother's renewal was complete.

Since the wind was no longer cold-sharp,
she threw off her robes,
to lie open and available to Father-Sun.

When the spilling rain came upon the land,
as a lover to the beloved,
she was made fertile,
and bore great abundance.

We celebrated the return of Male-Robin
who came to pull earth-worms.
After nesting,
our Chief received the blue egg,
as a thanks to Earth-Mother for new life.

Herbs and greens were cooked with fresh deer or elk.
Mushrooms,
dandelion greens,

bear grass shoots,
fern necks,
clover,
lupin roots,
cattails,
water cress
and mint
were some of our Growing-Season food.

With the sprouting of the willows
we began our ceremonies for the life forces around us
and celebrated our sexual play.

It was a time for telling stories,
usually of hope and sex.

This was the season for cleansing ourselves
and our homes.
We swept away the spider webs of talk,
with the same cedar branches
we had used to whip our bodies spiritually clear.

We were getting ready for action,
and,
after cleansing ourselves,
we went to sweating and bathing ceremonies.

It was a time to sing and tell stories,
while we sat near hot stones,
in our small half buried lodges.

Light was left out of this cocoon
and when we emerged
from the hot, cramped mud hut,
filled with cleansing sweetgrass smoke,
we were ready to swim in the cold
and enjoy action.

We sent songs to the clouds
and called for rain.
We invited the water
to walk out of sky's rainbow teepee flap.

After painting ourselves
with yellow-pine tree pollen,
we sang:
>"*Let there be big rain*
>*for the mountains and prairies.*
>
>*So the grass can be long*
>*and the berries many.*
>*Cover the earth with flowers.*
>*Make her seeds grow strong shoots.*
>
>*Send living waters,*
>*sacred wind*
>*and cleansing power.*
>*Happy we eat!*"

Then we danced
until earth shook from our celebration
and our flesh quivered with the beating drum
The men thumped the earth heavy,
with powerful down-pressing stomps.

Then with a strong lifting chant,
   "O-o-o-o-o-I"
they sang and danced
the throb of their heart drum-pounding.

It was a strong steady beat
calling for precise and dramatic action.

Ferociously they danced
feet pounding hard
rapid and violent;
until they shook Earth-Mother awake
after her long sleep.

The beating blood through earth,
called for new life.

The drums beat loud-soft-rest,
(repeated sharp, short beats
followed by total silence)
until Mother was awake.

Children blew whistles,
representing our Ancestors' voices.

In The-Season-Of-Growing-Things,
we shook rattles with a sudden shutter,
announcing Mother's awaking.

Then we all went into the fields,
calling for the flower spirits to arise.
We asked the life seeds to shoot up as sprouts.

On this Day-Of-Full-Moon,
during the Festival of Joy,
masked figures,
painted in cold grey ashes
from the village camp fires,
danced vigorously among the pollen covered dancers.

Moving in the opposite direction,
they carried dead tree branches
and dry grass clumps from seasons past.
with flexible muscle power
they continued to draw sleep from the earth.

They called juices from the roots
so they would climb
to meet the falling sky-waters.

If women got tired,
men rubbed them like black-horn bulls,
to give them new strength.
At the close of the dance,
men shot arrows deep into the earth,
as a sign of fertility and sex-power.

According to the depth of the arrow shaft,
our grandmothers choose a woman for
each to breed.

When Sun touched the highest sky peak,
on His journey along the horizon,
we had our great celebration.

We danced and sang without stopping
around our central tree,
around each village dwelling
and around special people,
such as our Chief, hunters, herb gathers, or
new mothers.

For a moon cycle
we claimed the land warmth
and celebrated to Sun-Spirit.
We had arrow shooting contests,
and guessing games,
where we used buffalo or antelope knuckle bones.

There were cooking contests
and celebration for new women.

New-quilled clothes were set before Sun.
There were wrestling matches,
hunting contests
and initiation rites.

We counted our victory-successes,
our bravery achievements

and recounted our prize physical strength.

We each danced our story:
The hunters, their good luck,
Medicine people, their experiences,
The Scouts, their adventures,
The lovers, their exploits.

Our music was more action than words.

It was the same for our everyday lives.

Naked,
except for smeared body paint,
men careened around camp
with free and vivid movements,
whooping and howling
    "Woo-oo-oo-oo-oo-oo-oo, hi, hi."

These were the fun makers
they were clever,
funny
and full of prancing horseplay.

Their mimicking hop-leaps in the air
were joyously funny
and their loud
"ho-ho's"
    entertained us all.

These wild-men taught us

to laugh at moons-past
and to use these experiences for aliveness-visions.

As Spirit-fools,
they called us to big fulfillment.
  "Hi-ya!
  Hi-ya!
  Hi-ya!"

III.

THE-SEASON-OF-YELLOW-LEAVES

When The-Season-Of-Yellow-Leaves arrived,
and we came to our lower hunting grounds,
we had another festival.

We gave thanks for what had happened
up to this point of our return.

We remembered acts of bravery.
We rewarded loyalty and noble care.
We renewed our vows with one another.
Men openly affirmed their friendship ties
by sharing their blood-life-waters.

We returned Earth-Mother's thanks,
as we sustained each other.
We thanked Wind for its favor.

We thanked the Dancing-Cloud-Maidens
and Grandfather-Sun
for rain and sunshine.

In this season,
as the hazel nuts and acorns fell,

NADA

Spirits returned to earth from the sky,
just as tree sap returned to the roots
and leaves dropped to the ground.

Often, we sat and sang to the rising moon:
  "Hi-ya! Ai Hi-yah!"

We followed the Spirit circle of the seasons,
weaving our lives in this earth-sky-basket,
preparing for our long camp near the earth.

A power song for this festival was:
  "Great Spirit,
  bless our friends
  through a long-happy life.
  We are your people
  and ask for your care
  with good hearts."

Our Sun-Going-Down dance was a quiet, tremulous hush,
just as the golden aspen leaves flutter easily
when they fall to earth-sleep.

Gently we waved their branches,
softly singing and treading easily,
until the dance moved lightly into darkness
and faded into the sleep of another season.

Sun's race would slow.
Shimmering stars would drum an easy rhythm,
which we felt in their vibrating twinkle.

PART V
CELEBRATION STORIES

*All this talk about festivities
and good medicine
is to say that these next stories
were part of our celebrations.*

HOPPING-EARS and MEADOW-MOUSE

One day I needed to have some rabbit medicine,
for one of the young men
who wanted to sire a special child
for our Ancestors.

We had some madrone leaves,
which we put between our thumbs and blew
to make the squeal of a baby rabbit.
The does came chasing out of their meadow burrows.

But. there were no bucks;
which we needed for the medicine.
Realizing the position of the sun was wrong,
we sat on an old log to wait.

This is the story I told him.

"Sun was out sky-climbing
while Hopping-Ears and Meadow-Mouse
were sitting on their haunches
talking about the weather
and the delicious Moose-Lake grass shoots.

Meanwhile,
Gray-Hawk came sky sweeping
for a skin-tail or hopper-ears meal.
But when hawk saw this opportunity,
he couldn't make up his mind
whether to have rabbit or mouse.

He was trying very hard to decide,
even during his dive.

It was a sure meal,
because mouse and rabbit
found their talk so exciting
that they had not taken care
to see Gray-Hawk's magic power,
even though Crow was warn-shouting.

Closer and closer he swooped
toward hopper and skin-tail.

Then,
with a swoosh-thump
he landed beside them.

To be sure,
they were surprised
at this peace omen from sky messenger.

As hawk came strutting over on his long sharp talons,
mouse smiled sweetly.

Meanwhile, rabbit was looking at hawk's large honed beak,
which could pull out an eye in one vicious peck.

Rabbit scratched his head with his crooked hind leg
and mumbled through his front teeth,
    'By the moon,
    what do we say to a hawk?'

    'Hello Mr. Hawk.'
Mouse squeaked.

    'Howdy critters.
    Looks like a fine day today.

    I was watching you
    and decided to join your talk.'

    'Well,'
responded rabbit,
picking up a small courage
to overcome his shyness,
    'we were just talking about food.'

Then he realized that,
in this situation,
it was not the best topic.

Mouse came in at just the right step
to say:
> *'And, also,*
> *we were agreeing with you.*
> *It is a fine day.'*

> *'Ha!'*
Retorted hawk.
> *'Food on a fine day is it?*
> *I remember when,*
> *on an ordinary day,*
> *I had slaughtered at least 20 mice*
> *and probably a good 10 or 15 rabbits as well.*

> *You know,*
> *hunting isn't what it used to be.*

> *I wonder if you critters*
> *are practicing some kind of sex control.'*
He then laughed deeply,
'Ha, Ha, Ha.'

It wasn't particularly funny to either mouse or rabbit,
but they grinned as a friendly show.
After all,
he was a guest!

'Tell me,
how is breeding these days?'

'Fine! Fine!'
squeaked meadow mouse
swishing his long skinny tail
and turning to rabbit for his answer.

'Okay, I guess.'
Rabbit said a bit quietly,
for he didn't usually talk about his sex life in public.

'All you furry little vegetable eaters
are just alike.' Squawked Hawk.
'You eat and have sex,
eat and have sex.
Does grass effect your sex life someway?'

'It gives us some privacy for play.'
Said shy rabbit,
thinking he could change the subject somewhat.

'Play? Ha! Ha! Ha!
What you need
is to do it in the air
and in the trees,
like hawks.

Do it on old stumps
and by the river.
Get freer in your self-expression.'

Rabbit was blinking wide eyed,
while mouse,
who was a bit of a sexual show off anyway,
was nodding his head in agreement.

'Well,
    thank you for your advice Mr. Hawk,'
was about all rabbit could stammer.

Mouse,
who had found his tongue
behind his straight white teeth,
said:
    'Mr. Hawk,
    do you really think vegetable-eaters
    breed more than hunters?'

'Well,
    let me give that a second glance.'
As hawk cleared his throat,
it sounded like the gravel in his craw
grated together.
It sent shivers along mouse's tail.

'We are looking at very different critters
in these two.
They smell different,
they act different,
and they live in very different lodges.

Hunters and vegetable eaters
might as well be mountains apart.

Of course,
if you take the two legged hunters
and vegetable eaters
they are in a separate valley;
for they can destroy all living things.

I guess you
aren't into all this disrespect-violence anyhow.
That's why you make such good food
for my little pinfeathers.
Ha! Ha! Ha!'

At this point,
neither mouse or rabbit was smiling.

Hawk realized his joke was a bit distasteful,
so, he shifted it to a note of thanks,
by saying:
    'Your care,
    in giving yourselves to the life cycle,
    is a noble example to us all.'

    'That's easy for you to say
    when you are next up on the cycle.'
Mouse said rather boldly.

    'I suppose so,
    I suppose so,'
hacked Gray Hawk.
    'But in life
    we are all the same.'

Off he flew,
leaving mouse with his mouth wide open.

    'How could he be the same?'
    He had never thought of himself
    as being the same as hawk or rabbit or person."

II.

PRAIRIE-OAK

One day Power-Man and I were in the prairie
getting onion medicine for skin sores.

When anyone got open sores
which did not heal,
we rubbed them with onion juice and hemlock tea.

After three-sleeps we bathed them
in water-poured-over-hot-stones.
Then we put a thin layer of pine rosin,
bees wax and bear grease over the area.

Before touching people with open sores,
I washed my hands in warm urine
as part of the cleansing ceremony.

It prepared me to touch them
without offending their health.

If the problem was boils,
we used a cooling plaster of bruised plants,
alternated by warm poultices made of acorn mush
and slimy ground fungus.

Skunk cabbage root was also baked in hot ashes.
We then slit it open and put it on the boils.
We let it cool for one sleep.

This drew healing to the skin
and made the boils drain.
Once this happened,
we washed them in dog-fish oil
and boiled ash-bark water.

While we gathered herbs,
dark sky clouds gathered the rain shadows
and stood in the open prairie.

As I listened,
I could hear the thunder of eagles' wings,
echoing from the cloud-mountain canyons.

Spirits were close by,
to help us gather well.

The grass gently swayed
in the puffing wind.
Rooted in earth,
grass was our most basic nation;
for all other nations depended on it.

The clouds called us to the Council-Tree.
It was here
that Spirit told us what herbs to use
and what council the Tribe needed.

This gnarled prairie-oak
had put its roots deep into the earth
and openly sky-stretched its limbs.

Through its branches,
Spirit voices whispered:
"Deep dig my roots in the earth."

Oak had stood alone for many moons,
as the tree of dreams.

It had 'Emptiness' for Brother,
Wind for Sister,
Spirit for Father,
Earth for Mother
and grass for friends.

Its simple presence,
brought fullness to all creatures.

Between oak and prairie
was an open trust.

Born of sky-earth,
they were both mysteriously made,
from sun and moon,
as they light traveled across the seasons.

They reflected the Star-Nation's council,
whose fires glowed in the night sky
and whose traditions are in Great-Spirit's heart.

I found that in Oak-Prairie
there was a mixed together balance
of light and shadow,
strength and weakness.

The easy peace between them
was the strength of All-Life.

All that was desired
the other fulfilled.

They had lived together for so long
that they did not know how to live apart.

This was to be my lesson in potent power.

Prairie was where sky-earth rested,
like a lover lying on the beloved.
Oak was where they met.
Medicine power came from
the sacred tree.

As I picked acorns,
for stomach medicine,
I heard the empty prairie whisper
fullness-contentment.
In the oak,
nature sang its fulfillment.

Life-wind
from the overshadowed sky
made tree stand strong.

Just as I must do for my people.
This was my big prairie lesson!

III.

WISDOM and LITTLE-STRIPES

One day a small boy,
who had just been initiated into our Tribe,
came along the trail,
kicking stones
and paying no attention,
other than to his discontent.

As I was returning from prayer,
he suddenly bumped into me.

I had been long watching this youngster,
for his father held high standing in the Tribe.
The boy's mother
wanted him to grow up to be well known.

It put a squeeze on the boy
to perform in ways that looked good
and made points with the other boys.

FACE-OF-THE-RISING-SUN

When he bumped into me
he became very afraid,
for his mother had taught him
to be careful of the power which worked through me.

Seeing his big fear,
I had him sit beside me on the trail.
As I told him the story of Little Stripes,
we had great fun together.

Here is the story:

    Great stone cave,
    which was Earth-wisdom's open mouth,
    was high up on Dog-Tooth-Cliff.

    Getting there was along a deep worn trail.
    Animals went to learn the Invisible-One's medicine.

    On one side of the cave
    was a clear spring,
    from where strength flowed.

    Owls came to learn wind calls.
    Mountain sheep and conies came
    to hear the soft bird songs at dawn.

    At high sun,
    Wisdom sat in council.
    One had to close their eyes to see her:
    Spirits are best seen in darkness.

NADA

No word was spoken,
for silence is Spirit's voice.

One day Wisdom said to Eagle:
"All things come from emptiness
and are cared for by silence.
The power which stands behind all-that-is,
remains unseen.
It guides all life,
but is unknown.
This Power moves all,
without getting in the way."

I told him that,
like coyote,
Wisdom was both a deceiver and a truth-teacher.

If we depended on our outside senses,
we were deceived by her.
If our inside wisdom was trusted,
we were filled with great mystery.

On our Wisdom-Quests,
we learned how power is the shadow of stillness.

To let confusion fly away,
we practiced letting go of things.

We gave up everything
so our lives could become sacred ceremonies.

FACE-OF-THE-RISING-SUN

I was watching the young man,
for I wanted him to know
that he had to please no one outside himself.

He was preparing to go on a Wisdom-Quest.
But without this knowledge
he would not succeed.

As he took hold of what I was saying,
I continued the story.

"So, all the creatures came,
believing their inside voice
and received Wisdom's medicine

.

One day Little-Stripes,
who was the smallest chipmunk of all,
decided to venture along Wisdom-Path.

No one from his Tribe
had ever traveled so far from their lodge fires.

But he set out on his journey,
with feet light as the wind;
not even thinking where the trail might go.

He never packed food.
He just prayed for seeds
to make his life-trail smooth.

He didn't even say good-by to his family.
He just hurried onto the trail,
his tail flick-fluttering in the sun light.

His eyes were open wide
to take in all the new sights.
In the big sun halo
he stopped often to smell new things.

Then he ran to a new rock
or sat on his tail,
looking far down onto the prickly forest below.
Down there,
the lake and streams were alive.

Mountain cliff echoed their voices,
as they floated through the tall trees.
When clinging cloud mists left the trees,
and began mountain climbing,
their moisture got his whiskers wet.

Their shade made traveling cooler,
but their white fluff covered his path
and he lost his light-sense.
The-Salal-Berry-Moon was up
before he found a grass sleep-clump.

Just in time
he heard,
     'Sniff.
     Sniff.'

Before his eyes were open,
he jumped into action,
hitting coyote's snout end.
The hungry beast back jumped,
so chipmunk was able to get behind a rock.

   'Ya-hooooooo!'

After the excitement of his heart
stopped pounding his chest,
he slanted his eye to squint
out of the tiny crack
he had squeezed through.

He could see owl,
moon outlined,
in the plum thicket.

After she twisted off her head,
she made her voice sharp and clear,
   'Come-on-out.
   Come-on-out!'

Even though a green-grey moon-light
poured over everything,
Little Stripes decided to wait
until he could see with bigger ease.
Pushing his rump into a rock curve,
he let his front legs hang over the ledge,
so that he could sleep a bit.

His stomach was snarling and scratching for food,
he prayed for sleep medicine.
His dream crowded sleep didn't let him rest
very well,
but he at least outwaited Owl!

When next he blinked,
the sky had grown yellow.

He was also eye to eye with snake,
who had slithered in,
out of the sun.
He hadn't even heard poison jaws
moving closer and closer!

His only escape way was to wait
until snake lowered its head
to sink its fangs into his back.

The courage-discipline to wait was not easy.
But he made his hind legs ready
to frog jump.

Just as snake's tongue
moved to an eye whisker from his nose,
its beady eyes got overcast.

It dropped its jaw.
It lowered its head,
and bared its fangs.

Whoosh,
like a humming bird,
chipmunk darted across snake's back
and barely flattened himself
enough to get through the tiny opening
between the boulder and snakes big long stomach.

As he stopped fast breathing from his
skinny escape,
he brushed himself off a bit.
Every muscle in his body hurt.
He was also very hungry.

Even though blue-haze smoked the day,
Sun had already rock heated the trail.
He looked for shade in a choke-cherry patch,
which was leaning into the wrestling wind.

Just as he made the leap,
hawk swooped down.
Two wing beats and a jump later
he would have been food!

He had to take better care
than he had been doing!

Every place was new adventure.

He was sure it was safe,
for he found many grass seeds
and some re-berried rose hips on which to gnaw.

Never had food tasted so good.
He even stored some in his cheek pouches.

His journey,
along the trail,
across the cliff,
was one escape-adventure after another.

Wolf wanted him for a chomp-bite,
bob cat pounced on him
and clawed him the same direction as his stripes.
After throwing him in the air a couple times,
Little Stripes was just able to get away.

Eagle tried to grab him twice.

At one spot,
a big boulder came mountain jumping
and dug a hole in the pathway
just a few hops in front of him.

Not only were there dangers,
but grey-sky decided to hang low.
Wind pulled at his coat.
Chanting rain danced all around him,
soaking his hide.
It also created lake-puddles across the trail.

There was the difficulty of not having a sleep place.
Besides,
this was getting to be a very lonely journey.

Why hadn't he at least invited
his big muscled brother?

At another point along the trail,
there was no food.

There were only rocks and more rocks.
And it happened during Day-Of-The-Hot-Sun!
He was very thirsty,
tired,
hot,
and hungry.
Feeling weak and tired from all this,
he was not as watchful as he needed to be.

His quick jerks got slow,
and Crow came to pull his tail.
She swooped down from his back side,
pecking and hollering at him.

He longed to be the clouds
and fly over the earth!

Finally, he got to some low-lying rock flowers,
and was able to hide behind them.

After what seemed like many moons,
he reached the great cave.

He was bones and skin.
He was so tired and hungry,
lonely and miserable,

that even his fleas had given up hope.
They were ready to find another place
to set up their lodges.

Baby cougar met him at the cave mouth
and slapped his skinny body
against a big stone.
Flipping him into the air,
as if he were a flying squirrel,
the kit grabbed his tail in her mouth
and walked over to the spring.

The only thing he could do
was struggle and squirm.

Rat came by,
saw Little-Stripe's problem,
and ran near the cat to get its attention.

The kitten let Little-Stripes drop on his head
in the water-grass.
Lying there. twitching trouble-shivers,
but unable to move;
his journey moons pushed before his eyes,
like ashes falling from the night-dancing sky-lights.

Flies and yellow jackets landed on his body,
until it swarmed like a kicked ant hill.
    'Hm-m-m-m-m.
    Buzz-Buzz-Buzz!'

When his dust-scattered thoughts settled,
and he came to himself,
he was lying in the middle of soft grass,
beside the flowing water.

He shook off the fly-bugs,
and,
in the cool shadows,
he drank a little water.
He ate two grass seeds
and fell asleep behind a large grass clump,
under an overhanging rock.

When he opened his eyes,
Wisdom was sitting in the cave light.
He blinked in surprise at her sparkle.
Could any creature be so lightful?

He ate some seeds from the dried grass stems,
sipped from the spilling waters,
and then crawled to her sit-place.

She looked at Little-Stripes;
his coat was a mess from not being cleaned.
His strength was only a wind whisper.
The darkness could wipe him away
with one swipe.

Even with his cuteness almost gone,
Wisdom held him to her heart,
saying:

'In one sleep
I will have words for you to eat.
For now,
take my strength-warmth
and find some seeds.'

With big energy
he bounced his way back
to the water-grass fire-weeds.

By the time he went to bed,
his stomach said he ate too much.
With a night's sleep
and some food in his belly,
his strength took new breath.

By the new day,
he returned himself.

Most of his twitching stopped.
His mind looked clear.
He was happy.

All morning he ate,
once every while stopping to scratch
his skin in the sand.
Then he washed for his meeting with Wisdom.

He watched her come to her seat-counsel,
and hoped to say outside what he felt inside.

Bear came for a short report.
Snake was next,
followed by Wolf
and then Eagle.

Little-Stripes watched
all the animals visit Wisdom.
Their talk filled his ears so much
that when his turn got there,
he forgot what he wanted to know.

As he came before her,
he felt alive in a new way.

> *'Come.'*
> She said.
> *'Sit near me.*
> *Wait until last.'*

He was happy-sad,
for he wanted her full attention.

But as he sat and listened to Rat,
Butterfly
and all the others,
he realized what a good offer this was.

Finally,
she said:
> *'Alright,*
> *since you have no questions,'*
(how she knew,

he had no idea),
'I have some things for you.
Your journey was stupid-foolish.

Any who are fit to receive what they seek,
get it.

It does not depend on their search.

Wisdom comes to those who easy-receive.
Not to those who push after her.

All your trail adventures
were little exercises,
so you could see past them.
Instead of going through them,
you avoided each one.

It shows that you are not alive.

You do not dance,
you only perform.
You are dead.

You lost what is you.'

Little-Stripes was turned upside down.
He tried not to show it,
but Wisdom laughingly said:
'Your upset is waking you up,
so that I can come to you.'

Now he really felt mixed about!

'Go.
Sleep.
Use my words as your blanket.
We'll talk again.'

He could not sleep because of what he had learned.
He thought his Venture-Quest as rather remarkable.

Now Wisdom called it a death-journey;
not a life walk.

Bear came in the early darkness
to meet Wisdom,
so, he took a nap while he waited.
He pulled the air over his nose so hard
it shook chipmunk's weak clump.

Next day light,
after all the critters had gone,
chipmunk climbed onto Wisdom-Rock.

He pushed down his yawns,
but Wisdom laughed at his sleepiness.

'Come.'
She said.
'We must talk.'

NADA

Today he had a question:
> *'If I have followed death rules,*
> *what are my life rules?'*

She smiled.
> *'Let's look.*

> *You must accept everything,*
> *and give up all.*
> *This is your life-walk.*

> *Next.*
> *Untie your thoughts,*
> *so you can be all that is.*
> *Letting go shows that you are trustworthy.*
> *Forget yourself,*
> *so you can fulfill your vision.*

> *You don't have to bulge your muscles*
> *to be impressive.*

> *Be bendable,*
> *like green grass,*
> *so you can be strong*
> *and sing even in a strong storm.*

> *Never try to make a change happen;*
> *everything has its cycle.*
> *You are a little earth ball.*

> *So be simple.*

> *Be still.*

Silence is Life's way.'

All this was a big surprise to chipmunk.
'Has my journey been a worthless Quest?'
He asked.

Wisdom laughed.
'No.'
She said.
'All creatures enter this life cycle, dying.
Once your death-journey is over,
life can begin.

You have made your death journey.
Now Life has come.

You must let go of everything you have called life.

By dying you will become alive.
By letting go,
life comes to you.'

'But what about survival?'
he asked.

Again, Wisdom laughed.
'That is no longer your concern.
Never again will you have a place
where hawk or eagle talons can grasp.
No more will you give death a chance.
You are now a creature of silence.'

IV.

HOLDERS of the SKY

One day when the camas were blooming,
Power-Man and I were gathering white camas bulbs.

These are poison.
So only two can be eaten during budding.
They cleanse the slime
one gathers from being inactive.

In the soft wind surging through the canyon,
after the storm,
Light and Wind were talking.

> LIGHT SHADOWS:
> *"It's a funny thing.*
> *People are blind*
> *and think they see.*
> *They only grope their way*
> *around the earth!"*

WIND SHADOWS:
"I know.
> *They see only darkness:*
> *The darkness of which we are made.*
> *I think they call you, 'things.'*
> *They call me, 'cloud flyer.'*

LIGHT SHADOWS:
"I am but a reflected shadow!
> *Even plant-flowers,*
> *in their breeding excitement,*
> *to show their ripeness for sex,*
> *sing their power to you.*

> *A song which bees and ants hear-understand.*
> *They dance to you,*
> *and ask you to carry*
> *the sweet-smelling fertility of their children.*
> *As they turn away from light,*
> *they carry my shadow,*
> *which people call color.*
> *To the blind,*
> *this becomes beauty."*

WIND SHADOWS:
"I'm sure that
> *if we tried to tell people this,*
> *they would think us crazy.*
> *How will they believe that*
> *your color-shadow rides my back?*
> *You shine on the rear of my wind,*
> *just as surely as do the sky clouds!"*

LIGHT SHADOWS:
"What do you mean?"

WIND SHADOWS:
"Clouds are the shadows
*   which ride on my behind.*
*   People watch them as storm omens.*
*   They don't ask*
*   what shadow-raindrops or feather-crystals might be."*

LIGHT SHADOWS:
"What tricksters white and black are
*   to the People-Tribe!*
*   That is why magpie is a good magician!*

*   White shadows the light,*
*   while black pulls it.*
*   When we shift a bit,*
*   people are attracted to the colors,*
*   and never think of the light.*

*   They walk in darkness,*
*   without knowing it,*
*   for they look at 'things' and 'color' as real.*

*   Black is their way of seeing light,*
*   for darkness is when light is seen,*
*   and shadows are no more.*

*   Because humans trust things,*
*   they refuse to open the tepee flap of darkness,*
*   to understand the face of light."*

WIND SHADOW:
"Our magic
     is our ability to have people believe
     that they can see through us.
     So, you filter light through you,
     as I filter things through me."

LIGHT SHADOWS:
"Let's give them a sign
     of our tricks."

WIND SHADOWS:
"Let's have it be as fragile
     as light and wind!"

LIGHT SHADOWS:
"You use your shadows to show moisture
     and I'll use mine to reveal light.
     They will never think it is real.
     Maybe they will use our sign as a good omen."

So, Light Shadows and Wind Shadows
whipped up their breath-cloud-children
into fluffy puffs.

Then they back-stepped,
so the overhanging sky would bring
light and moisture into a circle.

This drew sky-earth together
with a bridge
which they laughingly called,
"RAINBOW."

V

BLACKBIRD'S DISCOVERY

One day I was down by the lake
getting fresh willow scrapings
to pound into a mush
for pulling a nasty cut together as it dried.
Once this dried,
I would pour hemlock bark tea on it.

This way,
the spirit of Flexible-Willow
and the stable power of Hemlock
would bring easy healing for a strong life.

Out of my eye edge,
I noticed Big-Standing-Heron fishing nearby.
Blackbird had decided to watch
from his perch.

He wanted to see if Heron's diet
was what made her grow so tall and handsome.
If bugs made one short and black,
there was going to be a big change in blackbird's diet!

Heron was standing in her dignified stiffness,
shadow-reflecting in the slow water;
waiting and watching in stillness.

Her feathers hung over her shoulders
like a Chief's bonnet on celebration day.

Blackbird especially noticed
her long neck and standing sticks,
as compared to his short neck
and stubby, scrawny legs.

He had watched Heron land.
Her wing spread
was much longer than blackbirds biggest stretch.

And her beak!
It was longer than
how far their separate echoes
pushed across the lake.

Then,
in one quick flash
-faster than a blackbird's eye could blink –
Heron stabbed the water with her beak
and grabbed a swimming by fish.

She held it in the air.
Then,
with a juggle-juggle,
turned the fish head first,
and swallowed it in one big gulp.

It was a sickening sight.
Blackbird wanted to throw-up his own throat
and empty his craw.

How could anyone eat a slimy thing like that?
It would have to be in one slurp.
It was too awful to chomp.
One could see the thing slithering down Heron's neck!

It must taste as terrible
as bad smells stink!

Just as his stomach was turning over,
Heron looked over at him.

With a smirk,
she burped in satisfaction.
Then went back to fishing.

It all made Blackbird's feathers stand on end.
So, he fast found several crisp grasshoppers,
which had flown near the sun and colored their wings.

He mashed them in his beak and swallowed them.
He had to do something to forget Heron's ter-
rible food.
Then he ate some moist little critters.

When sun reached the sky middle,
Heron was forgotten.

Next, Blackbird spied Coyote
wading into muskrat marsh.

'Can you imagine eating a stinking muskrat?'
He thought almost aloud.

Just the thought of it,
made him seem like thistle down,
dizzy-circling in a swirl wind,
along with fir and bones!

Yuck!

Otters diet was no better
and certainly no one could live on Snake's!'

What it finally came to
was that each critter depended on the other.
One thing endlessly eating another.

Blackbird asked himself:
   'Is this the way of all creatures?
   There's got to be something more
   than eating one another!
   Life-sharing this way
   is much too shabby!'

That night,
as he held his cattail perch
near their nest,
he realized that they life-shared when they mated.

267

When they flew, and sang together,
they shared power.
But what pulled him together with everything?

With the flock,
the animals,
and even with the nasty fish?

When sleep darkness was strong,
and night was getting old,
as his mate sat on the nest eggs,
he woke up to her sleep breathing.

He realized that there was air power.
When we breath,
we share life.

> 'Maybe all our eating of one another
> is just a way of aliveness sharing!
> Giving one another our lives
> is like breathing
> and as easy as light or darkness,'
> he thought.

Next day he was singing:

> "Life for life
> I give!"

Hawk came by and asked Blackbird for his life.
But Blackbird told Hawk that he agreed to use it
for growing up his pin-feathered children.

After that,

Hawk could have his strength
for a flight to Land-Of-The-Sun.

PART VI
CHANGE CELEBRATIONS

I.

INTRODUCTION

When males could make life,
and females became carriers of life-power,
our people held Moon-Earth Change celebrations.

The young people were no longer call, *'Mother's-Children.'*
Mother's-Children was when people adventure-learned,
to choose-risk,
and grow-reach.

As a Mother's-Child,
each one belonged to the entire Tribe.
Anyone could teach them
and provide training in our traditions.

With sexual power,
their lives shifted.
They assumed duties
needed to keep the Tribe alive-together.

These duties were handed out
according to the person's abilities.
To find each person's talents,
our Council selected a teacher,
who became their spiritual parent.

For a moon cycle,
they lived together like relatives,
on sacred grounds for men or women.

During these days,
the teacher learned the strength
and weakness
of each person to be initiated.

The women returned when the moon was open
and the men returned when the moon was closed.
During this moon cycle,
they learned what the Tribe expected of them.

As a change-sign,
they wore their hair in two braids
rather than one.

II

WOMAN-WHO-KNOWS-THE-MOON

Women learned how to celebrate
their gift to bring new life into the world,
and to care for the awesome mystery
expressed through them each moon.

When this first happened,
it was a big celebration.
The girl sat in center circle,
surrounded by the women.

A Grandmother would turn toward the moon
and say this magic to Moon-Spirit:
   "O Woman-Who-Knows-The-Moon,
   All-Mother,
   Great-Life-Bringer,
   be present here."

Then,
turning to the girl,
she would sing of female mystery.

"May the sun shine upon you
all the days of your life."
(The girl's forehead was painted red.)
"May great blessings follow each day."
(Yellow pollen was placed on the red paint,
in three lines across her forehead.)
"With the stars,
may you see through the eyes of your daughters
and their daughters,
to live forever."

From now on,
during the release of old life blood,
and the renewal of life,
they would gather with the women
in a retreat lodge.

This was a time
when life-powers grew with the moon
and joined with Earth-Mother's fertility.
This scared resting place,
away from duties and family,
was part of the Tribal rhythms,
which tied us with All-Life.

Through this connection
women held our tribal mysteries
and carried the future abundance of our nation.

The women always held the creative force,
and were our connectors with Great-Mystery.

Women brought beauty
and new life into the world
Our people grew out of them.

Women of great presence and spirit held our Tribe together.
They were our strength.

During their moon time,
women did not prepare food
or take part in ceremonies or dances.

The only meat they ate was raw cow buffalo liver.
This was to help restore their blood.
They also drank tea made form fireweed root.
Otherwise,
they ate vegetable during this time.

This part of her life was not shared with men,
for she was so powerful during this time
that she could hurt the male spirit.

While with their older spiritual mothers,
the young women learned about our Ancestors,
waiting to be born from animal forms,
into our People-Tribe.

These Ancestors were waiting in sacred areas,
to enter a women's body,
so that when she was with a man sexually,
this life-form would develop as their child.

Our sexual life
involved the Ancestor's animal,
and was the way back to Over-Spirit.

She learned how to give herself to a man,
so that this sacred, creative power
was shared during breeding.

She learned skills for bringing life into the world,
how to care for Mother's-Children
and how to provide for her own infants.

Her family would give the gift of our teachings
and continue our heritage into other moons.
This was our way of creating care
for the Tribe.

She also learned her own wisdom,
quietly running in her blood.

The most difficult lesson for your women,
was developing ways to stay shy and quiet,
with modest eyes,
as is the custom of our people for women.

To show this,
she was to keep her feet close to Earth-Mother,
whose vital power she represented.
So, she danced with shuffling step,
as if wearing away the earth.

She also learning special skills,
which included:
basket weaving,
chipping stone tools,
gathering roots,
preparing food,
setting up lodges,
treating animal hides,
and making clothes.

When a woman was set apart from the Tribe,
for receiving Life-Spirit,
she was painted with red medicine paint,
representing their earth-bodies.

She was painted so the spiritual directions were honored.
As helpers lifted her above their shoulders,
they blew into her Spirit blanket
and called her newly born.

Once she was presented to the directions,
she was given new clothes and jewelry,
as a sign of her change-life.

Sometimes she received a new name.

We then washed her with camus meal
for her initiation ceremony
with the Elders and Grandmothers of our Tribe.

III.

MAN-MOON

With the Man-Moon,
for men left camp in pairs,
for the sacred-magic places.

With his nature-power,
each young man learned:
reserved restraint,
dignified courage
and peaceful pride.

In sacred rites,
he learned self-responsible action.

As an active man,
he also learned to enjoy his breeding stick,
and how to use it with women.

He learned
to be responsible for the tribal children,
to speak men's talk
and how to have a name for his child.

To choose the power of a name for someone,
was a difficult task.
The man had to help Animal-Master-Shaman
know whose Ancestor-Spirit
had come to make the child.

This way,
they could bring the name to life again,
and make predictions and sacred objects for the child.

This was done
so that life in the child could develop well
and our traditions be kept alive.

During initiation,
the young man had to learn
to show respect for tribal rules,
and how to be part of our rituals and traditions.

These were things he was to pass on to his child.
These were:
the gift of kindness,
reverence,
respect for every creature,
appreciation for all life,
thankfulness,
honesty,
the ability to live in peace,
and a respect for themselves
which let them speak out
for what is best for everyone.

Like water in the creek,
each man must learn to accept and carry
anything that came to him.

According to agreements with the Tribe,
he took a skill.
These included:
hunting,
planting,
fishing,
caring for and curing meat/fish/vegetables,
making lodges,
cutting canoes,
caring for livestock
and care of the camp.

Together,
the men discovered the young man's totem Ancestors
and developed a dance ceremony
celebrating their spiritual bond.

The paint decorations,
songs,
and dances,
all tied a person with his Ancestors.

Each man entered his Ancestor's life circle.
This made him full of power
and tied him to every living being.

His great totem discovery
was for the care-protection of the Tribe.

His personal powers came later.

When they returned to camp,
the young men and their trainers
gathered for a special initiation ceremony
with our Elders.

As a sign of his decisions and abilities,
he could now begin to wear feathers
other than plumes from over the bird's heart.

He also wore power objects,
such as claws or teeth of animals.
These were reminders of the tribal Spirit;
the Life-Spirit alive in him.

IV.

ENTER FROM LAND-OF-THE-SUN

For all initiates,
both men and women,
the Elders sat before a council fire,
with their backs toward Land-Of-The-Cold-Wind.

The initiated-one
entered the ceremony from Land-Of-The-Sun.

For the new ones,
this was a difficult meeting,
because our Elders
held the universe within,
and knew all inner secrets.

They could read the trails of one's thinking.
They could see through everyone.

The Elders were people of dignity,
integrity
and power.
They were links with our Holy-Ones,

who went before us.

They were the way-knowers
-the song
-the dance!

The one seeking a place in the Tribe,
sat before me
and selected power objects from a medicine pouch.
These objects were then placed
within a ground-circle design,
which represented our Life-Mother.

Each object represented powers
which guided their lives.
How they were arranged,
showed the person's life walk.

One of the Elders then read the design,
and provided council
which was to help the person for a lifetime.

The person had to look carefully
at the Mystery inside themselves,
until they were in balance with nature.
They felt that their face and belly were cut open,
until their heart was empty.

Once the ceremony was over,
the person was never again as before.

This change
put the person's fee on their life-path.
They knew their power Spirits
and how to listen to them for guidance.

These powers represented medicine strength
for their earth-journey.

In my lodge
the old men held the young men
while sacred cuts were made on their bodies.
This made their life blood returned to Earth-Mother.

Then sacred stones,
sticks
and charms
were given to the young man
for his purification,
safe-protection
and ability to perform in the Tribe.

The spirits of these emblems
were his life-guides.
Once he returned to the stars,
they were put to rest in his honor.

After dancing
and rubbing their bodies in cedar
and sweetgrass smoke,
each young man was sent up-the-mountain alone,
to find his own guiding and protecting Spirit.

Before being sent to this far-away place,
he was painted white,
red
and yellow.

In a vision,
he would find his protector.
This would be an Ancestor,
usually in the form of a bird or an animal.

He then had to find and kill his vision animal.
Then he took its robe for his medicine;
making part of it into a medicine bag.
This was a home for his totems.

This quest let him be born into Mystery-Spirit;
the great world for which all else is a starting line.

When nature was seen as his inside-self,
each man was given a new name;
a reminder of how to keep his vision alive.

He also received a Spirit song.
So that his Ancestors would be honored and free to live.

V.

POWER-WO/MAN

There were women and men
who did not seek these traditional roles.

They chose not to breed,
but to live as someone with two souls
-one man and the other woman.

They were assigned to Power-Wo/Man
who trained them in caves.

These lodge-caves represented Earth's center.
They spent many moons away from light.
The darkness trained them to trust their inside Spirit.

In these birth chambers,
they learned how to be guardians
of all living things.
They found what nurtured Mother
and what fed them.

They learned how to keep earth-sky in balance.
It was a powerful life dance,

keeping the earth-heart beating.
It kept Mother alive
and the earth from ending.

Life-fertility depended on them.
They understood nature's mind.
They fasted and prayed.
There were keepers of life.

These visionaries helped with the sick
and carried our customs and traditions in their hearts.

Without them the rain would not fall
and the earth would not be fertile.

They took care of us.
It took a special balance of wo/man
to understand Earth-Spirit.

Such a person helped all things grow and be healthy.
These medicine people gathered healing foods,
water,
and medicine plants.
They worked with Spirits,
and led in dances or ceremonies.

Sometimes these men took women's roles
and the women took men's duties.

Often, they were given visions of masks,
which they made and wore at our festivals.

These were Spirit-power masks,
used for purification rituals,
cleansing ceremonies,
and special times,
such as introducing or announcing tribal decisions.

Their role was to sustain the life of our people,
They had the powers
for continuing healing-health.

When they were initiated,
they were wrapped in sacred robe-blankets
and held above the heads of the helpers.

They had to completely give themselves to Spirit.

Their calls,
and deep visions
let us know when this was done.

For the initiation moons,
they were totally helpless;
just as children.

They never talked.
They were fed,
bathed,
and,
cleaned.

They never made decisions.
A guardian was given to them,
so their Spirit attention
would not be double vision.

They did not look at people.

They belonged only to Spirit.

If these medicine people were women,
special attention was made;
for women have great power.

Their power could draw energy from a man
and leave him spirit-dead.

This is the reason men,
who are given women's roles by Great-Spirit,
have special medicine powers.

Women who assume men's roles,
as medicine people,
are extremely powerful.

PART VII
HEALING STORIES

I.

WOLF-CRY FALLS

My lodge was always considered a sacred place.
Only on rare occasions
were there interruptions.

One of these was
when Chief came into my Lodge early
one morning.
Here is how it happened.

In the dawn darkness,
Chief awakened from a vision-dream,
which deeply troubled her.

Realizing this was important,
I asked Chief to sit down
while I stoked up the fire.

As tea was heating,
Chief told her vision-dream.
    "Porcupine was bark chewing
    the tops of each young forest tree.
    No tree was missed,
    as he made his rounds.

Deer and Elk,
along with Bear and Wolf,
were upset.

This meant the trees would die.
He was going to destroy the forest,
and nothing could stop him.

Wolf told the others,
'The power is in the water of Mighty-Falls.'
Deer and Elk thought this was strange medicine,
and bear just laughed.
But Wolf went to her den
and got her strongest whelp.
She picked her up by the neck
and ran to the top of Big-Rock-Mountain,
where she dropped the pup over the falls.

When Wolf got back to the bottom,
Porcupine was floating dead in the water.

So were the young men from the Tribe -
each one with a porcupine quill through his heart.

The forest was gone,
and the women had eaten all the seed-nut cones.

Even though Porcupine was dead,
the wide-open land made a desert.
Antelope and Buffalo left the plains."

As she stopped telling the dream,
I pulled out my pipe
and put together some sacred herbs.

I put sage on the fire stones,
and said:
> *"This is the meaning of your dream.*
> *When our people awaken,*
> *some of our young men will be ill.*

> *They will die.*

> *This will continue until our men are gone.*

> *The only change-medicine*
> *which will work,*
> *is if a maiden from the Tribe*
> *is willing to give up her life for our people."*

Chief did not give this solution
the worth of a bird's head.

> *"Let's wait and see what the day brings."*
She said to me.

By twilight some young men were ill.

After one sleep, they were dead.

Chief said nothing to the Tribe.
By the end of a moon cycle,
many more had died.

The tribal council met,
and decided to tell the people
about the medicine I said would work.

It had to be a sacrifice of care,
rather than a tribal decision.

The one who had to choose was a pure maiden.

In one sleep,
our bravest tracker became ill.
He was secretly admired
by the most beautiful woman of the Tribe.

She was Chief's daughter.

She had hoped
to sometime share a teepee with the tracker.
After hearing that he was ill,
she left camp alone.

Knowing she could not live to breath hard with longing,
she decided to place her life
beyond the naming of want.

Just as the sun came over the mountains,
she sang a love song:
  "As day follows day
  we shall live together."

The she gave herself to Spirit-Of-The-Falls.

As Sun traveled alone to the evening-land,
they found her body in the pool.

Next day,
the man she loved
put sweetgrass ropes around her neck and wrists.
He buried her on a nearby mound,
and prayed to Spirit-Of-The-Falls
to bless her for saving him and the Tribe.

In lonely sadness,
he built a fire on top of the mound,
which he hoped would steal his sad thoughts.
It was his way to let the passion-flame burn
and the sorrow-embers die in the ashes.

As Sun went away
he sang a river song to her soul:
  "Let the hard rocks pass
  along the river banks.
  Oh, gentle soul.
  Oh, gentle soul."

NADA

Today,
if you silently listen,
the cave behind the falls
echoes Wolf's call,
as she cries for her pup.

II

NIMBLE-FINGERS and the GREEDY BEARS

The traditional way for women in our Tribe
was the path of peace.

Theirs was the action
of bringing together-unity.
Their role held the Tribe steady,
no matter what happened.

In thinking of how complete this was,
I think about Nimble-Fingers.

One day she was in the forest
picking black berries for the Tribe.
From behind the bushes,
Grizzly-Bear suddenly stood up on his hind legs.

He was so big
that Nimble-Fingers looked like an ant beside him.

"What are you doing
in my berry patch?"
He growled.

"Well,
I saw your fresh and heavy manure piles
and thought this must be a good berry patch."
She replied.

"Those piles mark my territory,
and for your invasion of my eating grounds,
I demand all the berries in your basket."

Very well,"
she said,
without giving his comments another thought;
for she was comfortable giving everything she had.
"Why don't we sit in the shade,
and you can eat the berries I have picked."

Bear seemed happy with this,
and they went to sit in the shade.
He ate every berry in the basket.
When he was through,
he licked his chops
and sniffed for more.

"Do you want me to pick more berries?"
She asked.

"Well,
I wouldn't mind if you do."
He said
yawning wide.
"I'll just make a little sleep while I wait."

Soon he was scratching air over his nostrils;
while Nimble-Fingers was picking berries in the sun.

The briars were sharp
and stuck her legs and arms.
But she kept picking;
this time with bear's permission!

When she had filled the basket,
Black-Bear came along
looking for food.

Thinking this was an easy meal,
he said:
"Huf, Huff,
I want that basket of berries."

"I have nothing to say about it."
she replied.
But before she could talk more,
Black-Bear became angry.

He beat on a nearby fir tree
with such big thumps
it awakened Grizzly from his nap.

As Black-Bear came running toward her
to get the berries,
Grizzly jumped to his paws and charged.
The deep thump of their meeting
knocked their eyes upside down,
and rolled them end over end
into the berry patch.

They fought tooth and claw,
while the briars held them tight.
Each one thought the other was holding him down,
and fought more than usual.

Each one was close to death
before they saw what was what.
But Nimble-Fingers was not able to help them
out of where their greed had got them.

By now,
the sun was steady over head.
Some young hunters came
through the forest empty handed.

  "Come my brothers,"
    she said,
as she met them on the trail
with her basket of berries.
    "I have two Great-Ones-Of-The-Forest
    for you to take to camp."

They laughed at her,
and sat down to eat from the basket.
She knew her place,
and went back to the berry patch.

Both bears were dead.

She had a kindness for all life,
so, sang to them,
as she took a flint
and began to take off their skins.

When the hunters came down hill,
the bears had given her their Spirits,
as a give for her lesson in generosity.

When the men saw her,
they knew her greatness
was everything they hoped to be.

Taking two long limbs
they hauled the Great-Bears into camp.

None of the men could tell their story,
for they were taken into Chief's lodge.
Everyone thought they had done this great kill.
The entire Tribe gathered to feast and celebrate.

As the young men came out of Chief's lodge,
they received the praise of great heroes.

No one even noticed Nimble-Fingers,
working beside the crackling fire of burning spruce
and the pile of river-washed cooking stones.

She was rendering the bear grease
and cooking the meat.

She worked with reverence
for the souls of the ones
who were now giving their bodies to her people.

With a new mountain sheep horn-paddle,
she stirred together honey-berry cakes
for the celebration feast,
and cooked them on the outside fire embers,
which were slowly clouding over with grey,
like a dead hawk's eyes.

The cakes were thank-offerings to Great-Spirit
for the gifts she had received.
They were also her appreciation to the bears
for having become her medicine power.

Chief took the first bit of food
and spit it on the fire saying:
    "To you,
    Mystery-Powers,
    we offer this food.
    As soon as you have eaten,
    We also shall eat.
    Make us strong."

Then the people feasted and feasted.

When the celebration reached its big point,
the women who had worked on the bear skins,
brought them in as a gift to Chief.

Nimble-Fingers left camp
and went to a silent place no one could find.
Here she put sweet smelling cottonwood-punk
in her hair.

While she was alone
a supernatural visitor came to her and said:
"Hello,
Honored-One-Of-Great-Purity-And-Beauty.

You have been noble in your ways.
You have done everything in a gentle manner.

You have not been jealous for high praise
nor for a position with your people.

You have been wise beyond your moons.
Your life has showed the tradition-ways of women.

The gifts of Great-Spirit
are bestowed upon you.

The joy of earth-sky is your song."

Nimble-Fingers returned to camp,
glowing with her sacred visitor's presence.

She was openly beautiful,
for she was humble
and not self-puffed-up.

She did not realize she had become star beauty.
But when I saw her special shine,
I asked her to do a celebration.

She had the drummers change their beat
to a slow, quiet throb,
so she could sing a love song to the bears.

The song's walk was:
  "Mighty-Ones of forest height
  to you we sing tonight.
  Great you are in all our sight.

  Majesties-Of-Wondrous-Light,
  to us you bring delight.
  Great you are in all our sight."

It was simple,
yet perfect.

Chief let tears roll down her cheeks.
We knew Nimble-Finger's secret.

After she and I led the Tribe in a victory dance,
around the last glowing embers of the fire,
everyone but Nimble-Fingers went to bed.

She was last to leave the fire;

where she prayed:
> *"May this fire,*
> *as a sign of the All-Above,*
> *be the fire of my children*
> *and my children's children."*

It was deep darkness
and all except for Nimble-Fingers,
were asleep.

She did not want her perfect day to end.
Just as she closed her eyes,
she heard:
> *"Great deeds are done*
> *by those who are willing*
> *to remain unknown."*

III

FLUTTERING-WILLOW-LEAF and SILENT-PAW

Fluttering-Willow-Leaf was having a very hard time
making decisions.

She felt there was always a second voice
inside her ears,
giving her advice
which pulled her another way.

The voice was so strong that she was confused
and often ran around like Coyote,
without sense.

She had gone to many medicine people,
saying that when she moved,
her soul would go wandering.

Every time she had stopped the healing
because she was afraid it might end her life.

One day she came to my teepee,
and asked for help with her mixed-up-confusion.
She said uneasy ghosts were turning her eyes upside down.

We agreed I would present her to the direction-powers.
Then she was to go work in the field
with the other women.

After turning her in all directions,
for power guidance,
I chanted toward the Land-Of-The-Rising-Sun:
> *"Life-Growth comes*
> *from rising sun power."*

I sprayed yellow clay on her body,
to represent the clear, shining-sun sky.

Turning her to the Land-Of-Always-Warm-Sunlight,
I chanted:
> *"Warm wind, bring us food."*

Chanting to the Land-Of-The-Setting-Sun,
I sung:
> *"From the mountains*
> *the pine incense comes,"*
(I threw rosin on the fire and hot stones.)
> *"and the small shells, of long life."*
(I rattled shells in the rising smoke-incense).

Chanting toward the Land-Of-The-Bite-Wind,
I sung:
> *"Our strength is from the Star-Which-Never-Moves."*

Then I called on Grizzly-Bear power.
This had to be done with great care,
for Grizzly power
can be easily offended.
Then it becomes destructive.

Chanting toward the stars,
I sang:
"We have come from the stars
and to the stars we shall return."

Toward Earth I chanted:
"Oh Mother,
with good heart
we thank you for life."

To have Fluttering-Willow-Leaf
be in touch with her deepest self,
I sang her Spirit song,
and closed with:
"Bring joy to Fluttering-Willow-Leaf's faithful self.
Guide her to peace of heart."

To close the purification dance,
I sang:
"Hear us Great-Spirit.
Help us.
Grant us life.
Look with pity upon Fluttering-Willow-Leaf.
Drive away all illness.
Bring health to her spirit."

Once this simple but powerful ceremony was completed,
I sent her to the field.

The women were in the open meadows,
gathering camus bulbs to dry for the cold season.
Bending over a digging stick was hard
and Fluttering-Willow-Leaf soon got tired.

So, she went to the nearby forest
to get out of the hot sun.
This left the others to do her work.

While she was asleep on the moss,
beside a great stone,
she felt the presence of Silent-Paw.

Now Silent-Paw was a giant beast
who came to set things into harmony,
if, they were out of step with nature.

Half of him was walking about the earth
looking for his other part inside people.
He was able to hear his voice in the forest,
but no answer returned.
So, on the outside he was silent,
this was why the name, 'Silent-Paw.'

But on the inside
he could be heard walking about,
by the people of whom he was a part.

To set things on their earth-course,
he went seeking his balance
from the people who were out of harmony with life.

He knew that together
they had what would bring wholeness to them both.
Because he was not all there,
and because people who hid part of him inside
were afraid to let go of their secret,
he was considered a very bad enemy.

Fluttering-Willow-Leaf was very afraid,
because she could hear Silent-Paw inside her heart:
pounding around wanting to get out.

She knew that he had come
to put their lives in order.

But she clung to that part of him,
which she had grown to believe was part of her,
and refused to let it go.

She was held by her holding.

So, half-beast put his face over the rock top,
where she was,
and asked for the thing inside her
which kept her split apart from life.

It was a terrible inside wrestle.

FACE-OF-THE-RISING-SUN

She had held to this as her own name.

It was her private secret.

Silent-Paw finally pounced on her
with all his force.
He found the part of himself he was seeking
just under her lower ribs,
waiting and longing to get out.

Her pain was like child birth.

When he was gone,
she felt as if she were the person who had been born.

She heard a single twig break in the forest,
and knew she was her own blissful earth-sky harmony.

She went back
and began root digging in the field,
looking as if she had wrestled with the brambles.

She never again heard a second voice in her ears;
his echo never returned from sunrise to sunset.

Her heart became open.
She was no longer a stranger to herself.

315

As she picked up her digging stick,
she began to sing:
> *"The root is sacred.*
> *Where I dig is sacred."*

The women were so impressed with her change,
that they gave her a new name.

THE VISION OF CROW AND SWAYING-MARSH-REED

Many moons before my role in the Tribe,
the story of Crow and Swaying-Marsh-Reed
had been among our people.
It tells how our Sundance began.

Early one dawn,
as the high mountains
were scratching shadows across the sky,
and Sun was jumping the deep-dark-well,
Chief was bathing his feet in the drying grass dew,
on his way to stand before the rising sun.

Coming toward him,
on the trail,
was his deep-loved son,
who had been on a long journey.

His son ran to him
in great excitement,
his arms upraised in happy-peace.

Chief also had his hands raised,
with palms toward yonder sky,
for Sun was just jumping over the hill
from where the boy was arriving.

Without attention to the new day's dawn,
the young man stepped before his father
with joyful eyes.

He was met with Chief's upright lance
and over-shaded face.
>*"My son,*
>*you are my love,*
>*and, also my death.*
>*In your zeal,*
>*you held your reverence for the new day.*
>*Nothing can prevent us from such respect.*
>*Nothing can block the life-giving path,*
>*where Father-Sun comes.*
>*You must kill me,*
>*as an homage to The-Spirit-Which-Moves-In-All."*

With this command from his father-Chief,
the young man turned pale-face.
All greetings dried on his lips.
Not to obey would be disrespectful
to both his father and his Tribe.

Vowing they would not be apart,
the boy took his father's lance
and thrust it through the old Chief's heart.

Then taking its blood tip,
he fell upon it,
driving it into his own heart.
Together they entered the sun's gateway.

Those who were with them,
formed a circle around their bodies
and took them to the ridge top
where Sun danced every morning.

They took big stones
and piled them on top of their Chief and brother.
Their hearts were as heavy as
the rocks they lifted.

It was a big loss to the Tribe.

That day Sun stepped behind Moon,
shading earth with Great-Mystery.
That night great lights danced in the upper sky.

As the moons passed,
Sun burned with strong embrace upon the earth.
Grass withered in the day-fire.
Heat danced on the Plains.

Water holes dried up.
Rivers stopped their flow.
The soil became blowing dust.
The land was lean from longing for water.

Without moisture,
members of the Tribe died.
Vegetables and animals went away.
No longer was there food.

Faith flew away.
The people had lost their medicine.

Life was leaving the earth.
The hills were empty.
Even the sky seemed wrinkled.

One day Swaying-Marsh-Reed went to their watering hole
to collect the last water-drop.
She found it dry.
There was no shade anywhere.

Dust swirled like grasshopper clouds
in the empty land where,
in her childhood,
water had flowed freely.

As she looked across the hungry emptiness,
to the up-turned edge,
where sky-land met,
she thought about far moons ago.

The lakes were deep.
The rivers ran full.
Trees and vegetation were everywhere.
Food was easy to find.

While having this dream-vision,
a Sacred-Presence stood beside her,
dressed in Crow-Mystery.

Swaying-Marsh-Reed did something
almost never done by our people.
She asked a direct question.
    "Crow,
    tell me.
    What can save my people?
    I will make any gift,
    even my life."

Crow said:
    "Have your people receive Sun into themselves.
    Since the monument-rocks were piled on top of each other,
    they have rejected it.

    In the darkness of their own eyes,
    they lose their way.

    Tell your people that whatever curses
    is also their blessing.

    The place of crisis is sacred.

Remember.
Everything turns to Sun for life-growth.

It makes the trees ripen
and the grass to robe the green plains.
It makes people thrive.

Sun is the center pole
which up-holds the earth lodge.
It is a friend to your people."

"That it be so!
That it be so!"
Marsh-Reed said aloud,
feeling that her vision was given
to someone too small to make it happen.
"How do I get Sun into my people?
They need understand-strength."

"Come.
I will show you." Said Crow.
Together they went to rock monument.

Crow told her,
"Take all these boulders,
and make a circle around camp.
A circle represents Sun power.
It is a sign of each person.
The circle brings All together."

So, Swaying-Marsh-Reed worked at moving the rocks.
They cut her hands and made them bleed.
She held her face to the front,
even when it was hard to stay.

Before her task was done,
she received many bad words
for her 'foolish circle.'

She felt naked and without anything,
like an earth worm.

It is not easy to be wise alone.

They pyramid rocks had become a holy place,
where loyalty vows were spoken.

By the last day,
when only four pyramid rocks were standing,
she was called before the Council,
to see if Sun had set her thought to wandering.

Even though she felt like a wilted plant,
her mind was as clear
as a running stream on an easy day.

The-One-Mystery was at her center,
So, she stood with honor.

Her voice was not loud
but it covered everyone.

From the strength inside,
she held the palms of her hands into the sky
and said:
> *"All that moves in the sky;*
> *earth and sun,*
> *hear me speak."*

Turning to the Council
she said:
> *"Hear me even if my voice is feeble."*
By the time she was through talking,
they knew that she had not lost her thought-strength.

She told them about her vision
and how it was right for her to live her dream.

She also told them that the Tribe was to receive Sun.
Even though they said that 'their ears were open,'
most treated her like trail dust;
surging past her in the wind.

But two young men,
and one who was old,
made their hands ready.

> *"Come."*
They said.
> *"We will help you.*
> *If you speak with a straight tongue,*
> *it will save our people."*

They helped her roll the last rocks into place,
which made the camp a sun-circle.

But when Crow told her to take the sacred bones
of Chief and his son,
and to bury them around the land,
the three helpers refused.

They said:
    "All things have their place to be."

Standing on a lonely hill,
she knew she had to do this,
even if only with Crow's help.

She put the rib-bones in the ground as trees.

Their backbones were scattered in the dried
river beds.

The skulls were put in the low areas,
where medicine lakes had been.

The arm and leg bones
were reverently placed on mountain ridges,
as if the arms and legs of Chief and his son
were around them in a circle.

After this was done,
and the sun had, mercifully, hid behind the hills,
Crow said:

"The people must celebrate
with a life-renewal dance.
They must circle the tree of festivals.
They are to dance
until their chanting magic
releases Sun's hold on the land.

Their dancing will create sweat
which will remind Sun
to bring moisture with dryness,
and to make shade clouds
to cool the land."

Swaying-Marsh-Reed went to the three council members
for help in calling the people to a Sundance,
for earth's renewal.

But no one would call a celebration.

Dogs sprawled in the sun,
once in a while, biting at some flea.
The wind did not stir the dust,
even on the dry land sloping toward the mountains.

People's hearts were like the stone pile.

So, she took their last buffalo water-bladder,
and prayed:
    "Make the mistakes of my people
    go under the earth.
    Swallow all memory of our neglect.
    Make my people live."

Then she began to dance alone,
around the center pole of the earth.
She was singing:
 "There is a noise
 against the echo.
 Ya-a-ay!
 Ya-a-ay!"

As she danced,
flesh dew-drops spilled from her skin
and wet the ground.

When several men
tried to get the buffalo bladder from her,
they too were circle-moving.

People laughed at their funny dancing
and joined the celebration.

Someone with a drum began to chant.

When Sun heard their call,
and saw them dancing,
he was happy to be received as their inside fire.

He joined them
and began to sweat.

The ground became damp.
The rising steam made mountain-piled clouds.
As they grew taller,
they spilled rain.

The planted ribs drank their fill
and became forests.

The skulls filled with water and became lakes.

Rivers heard Big-Water's call,
and ran back to their home.

The arms of our Ancestors
reached around the land.

Then people saw
the wonder of Swaying-Marsh-Reed's vision.
They praised her for courageous steadiness,
even when they made it difficult to follow her vision.

Her only comment was:
    *"The day of the Sun
    has been my strength
    to do what is to be done."*

Now,
when Sun is hot,
we do a renewal dance.

It is a magic-way to show our sun power.
It is a new life dance,
where all things are made over.

Our young men slash themselves
as a mark of fortitude
and run around the sacred tree,
planted in the center of camp;
giving their life strength to Father-Sun
for his new race.

In this sacred life renewal dance,
each runner extends his full strength,
until sun's horizon-race is completed.

This is a race of each person against their own flesh.

This center tree,
whose top pierces the sky world,
signifies our central spiritual presence.

A person with two souls
honors the Tribe
by placing a medicine bundle high on top of the pole.
The bundle always contains two knuckle bones,
one of Chief and one of his son.

They protect the dancers who cut themselves
to share their life-streams blood,
for the good of our people.
It is their commitment
to take care of all living things for Father-Sun.

V

ARROW-SHAFT-MAKER

In our camp,
there were as many medicine people
as you have fingers on one hand.

We all worked together,
for our abilities were different
and our roles fit according to the people's needs.

I had the least number of requests
to help deliver children.
But some seemed to be so remarkable
that it felt like my responsibility.

I remember one sleep-darkness,
Power-Woman was asked to help
with a difficult birth.

The mother would not give up her pain.
To stop her insides from trembling,
and let her work be easier,
Cord-Cutting-Woman was having her mouth breath.

Medicine Woman brewed some fennel tea,
in which she ground a snake rattle end,
which the woman drank between muscle changes.

When Life-Giving-Mystery was present
with a new born child,
the new-cut cord,
was an important life-gift.

Cutting the cord and tying it far enough away,
so the child never filled with air,
was a ceremony.

We put goose fat on the cut
and the father took the cord
to make a bracelet for the child to wear.

Since this mother did not know the father,
he was not there to help name the child.
So, Power-Woman went through the naming ceremony.
That which spoke to her,
after the boy's Spirit-presence arrived,
became his name,
and that was,
"Arrow-Shaft-Maker."

In a special dance,
she held him to the Spirit-Wind messengers,
which bring life and strength.
Holding him near to herself,
she whispered his name.

Once Chief and the Council agreed to the boy's name,
he was accepted as a tribal member
with this prayer:
　　"Great-Sun-Father,
　　here is a child given to us.
　　Let us bring him to full man.

　　Bless him with favor.
　　Strengthen his hand.

　　Give power to his prayer medicine.
　　Look with good face upon Arrow-Shaft-Maker,
　　who we receive into our Tribe.

　　Make him generous
　　and heart good.

　　Let him always speak truth.
　　Fill the moons of his life with peace.

　　Make him a big life.
　　Help him not stumble along his life trail.
　　May his light-path bring many good friends.
　　Let him live many moons."

The test of acceptance into our Tribe
was how well he lived our customs
and entered our sacred ways.

He showed by his actions
the path by which he approached
the Supernatural.
This was the strength of his name
and his role in our Tribe.

In the Tribe,
we shared our lives as one soul.

Our ties reflected our Ancestors,
as they lived and spoke in us.
We kept them alive
so that the Tribe lived in harmony with wisdom.

As a
'Mother's-Child,'
Arrow-Shaft-Maker ran in the meadows
catching grasshoppers,
and swam in the waters
that brought the salmon home.

He filled his eyes with the mountains
and his heart with the sky.
Joy-freedom moved his blood.
He danced with the grass.

Sun power-shone his life.
He lived easy.
His way was peaceful.

NADA

As a child,
he made beautiful clothing designs.
From power-dreams,
he found that new pussy willow buds
made red dye;
buffalo gall stones made yellow;
and dry duck droppings made blue.
He made glue from boiled beaver tail.

When he became a man
he made special paint
from red and yellow earth,
for our dance-around-the sun.
The special white okra,
from clay and goose grease,
became our traditional purification paint.

He made the powerful black paint
from burned stems of the-thorn-bush-with-big-leaves.

He taught us to pull off our individual lives,
and robe ourselves in earth clay.

At festivals,
and on special lodges
he made our design stripes.

By making our outside and our inside one,
we had mighty power,
which went beyond earth limits.

When we shifted our thinking,
we heard our Ancestors' voices.
We were moved to a new place,
and when we reached that place,
we thought the thoughts of Great-Spirit.

We felt and saw life-strength.
We became Sun-light.
As we shined,
we established the wisdom of our Ancestors'.

Arrow-Shaft-Maker helped us explore all this.

Even in our ceremonial caves,
he painted spirit symbols,
inspiring us to holy things.

On our teepees
he painted our protection animals,
for supernatural medicine power.

By painting his vision on our bodies,
lodges
and clothes,
he fastened us with Spirit
and with one another.

To help us pull ourselves together,
with the heart beat of Earth-Mother,
he made our dance rattles.

NADA

The sea shell rattles,
for the women's dance,
matched the jingle of their dress fringes.

For hunters,
he made hoof-tree rattles
from mountain goats or deer.
These matched the straps of hollow hooves
tied to their ankles.

In our new-life dance,
we rattled buffalo breeding sacks,
and wore our black and white skunk-fur moccasins,
which were beaded with porcupine quills.

Our Dance-Of-Colored-Leaves
was celebrated with dry-gourd rattles.
Our men wore fox-skins;
swaying between their legs.

In all these ways,
he showed us how to open ourselves to Spirit.

With him,
we learned to sing,
so that the voices of our drums played many rhythms
and became the pounding heart of Great-Spirit.

He taught us how each person has a special song,
that put us in step with Star-Nation.

Arrow-Shaft-Maker lived many moons
and had many friends.
He taught us how to be one-face
and speak with one-voice.

VI

EAGLE-FEATHER'S CANOE

One day Eagle-Feather came to the medicine lodge,
saying he had been selected by his friends
to find a canoe-tree for the Tribe.

By himself,
in the woods,
he had spent four sleeps
without food or water.

Now he asked me for a cleansing ceremony
and guidance in finding the tree.

Taking a twist of sage,
I smoked it in the center circle of the lodge.
He then sat in this sacred place,
on a silver fox fur.

He stayed there four sleeps,
drinking only cedar, fir and hemlock tea.

Each day one of his friends came
and performed a water bird dance around him.
Then they placed white clay on his head,
to clear his thoughts.

For courage,
they covered the clay with down,
taken from over a water-bird's heart.

Each day I sent my voice to the four powers
  "Hey, Hey!
  Hey, Hey!
  Hey, Hey!
  Hey, Hey!"

These powers are one power,
and I said to them:
  "Before you,
  no one has ever been.
  You made the Star Nation to guide us;
  the Animal Tribes to show us the way;
  the Seasons to bless us;
  and all things to help us live.

  Bless Eagle-Feather
  to be part of all you have made.
  Lead him.
  Help him find the tree
  whose end will bless our people."

NADA

After Spirit's voice arrived,
and made pictures before his eyes,
Eagle-Feather stripped naked.
I hung a golden eagle feather
before his face,
so that he would remember his vision.

As he left my lodge,
I put an otter skin around his waist.
It was fringed with crow feathers.
On his head was a red-feather-bonnet
made from the tree-pounding-bird.

This would help him find his Vision-Tree.

In the clear sounds of dawn-light,
Grouse was puffing his chest
and drumming his song.

A wind,
from the beginning of life,
brushed through the bulrushes.

A loon cry echoed over the lake.
It was a brave fishing spirit.

Where White-Dirt-Creek became Spirit-Lake,
Crow-Tribe was holding a council meeting.

A silver fox went trotting along the path,
under them,
and up through the birch trees.

To Eagle-Feather,
these were good omens.
They showed him where he had to go
and told him what he had to do.
They were leading him to the tree
which had prepared itself to be a canoe.

During its life,
the wood had grown for endurance-strength.
Its shape had grown for water ways.

But even after all these conditions were met,
the tree had to agree,
to give its life for his people.

If Tree-Spirit was willing
it would let Eagle-Feather know
in some very clear and simple ways.

So, Eagle-Feather,
listening to the canoe song
singing inside him,
followed silver fox
until the trail moved apart in the woods.

A swirl of dry leaves played in the wind.

He waited until Black-Bear led the way he was to go.

NADA

When he found an eagle's feather,
with a wind-prayer playing along its breath-like edges,
it was his sign to move from the trail
and hike along Yellow-Jacket-Ridge.

He was scouting for the tree
where the one perched
whose feather he now wore in his hair.

He would recognize it
from a vision he had
while sitting in the center circle
of the medicine teepee.

Wind sang through the trees
with a voice of many sounds.
From where he stood,
he could hear the singing tree.

Then he found it,
in a small village of large trees.
A golden eagle was perched on the top limbs.

Life flowed full and strong through every branch.
Just as he reached its foot,
Sun came from behind the clouds
with a bright fire light.

Eagle-Feather laid his otter skin on the ground
and sat down to listen-wait.

His beaver wisdom
helped him become one with Tree and its Tribe.
He must share their talk
and hear their voices.
It had to be Tree-Spirit's and Tree-Council's decision.

Tree chose to give itself,
but the Tribe held its breath to let a member go.

At last they agreed.

They set a moon time with Eagle-Feather
to return with two young men
and receive their life gift for a canoe.

When Eagle-Feather returned with his friends,
the heavens poured a water blessing on the trees.
Spirit-lightning touched the air.

That sleep a round moon came
to take over the night.
It shadow-lighted every water drop
hanging from the forest leaves.

It was long before sleep caught them,
so, they had little rest before rising with the sun.
As the black shadows grew grey,
sun poured itself over the tree.

With special thanksgiving markings,
the men began their prayer-talk:

NADA

"We know your life
is as precious as ours.

We know we are all children
of Earth-Mother and Father-Sun.

We know one life gives way to another,
so the Great-Life can be sustained.

We seek your permission
to this killing.

We seek your consent."

Once this was assured,
and their rhythmic chopping began,
they sang,
    "O, Great-Friend,
    thank you for your blessing to our people.
    Thank you for the new life
    you will live with us."

Each tear of their axes
was an action of deep respect.

When the tree fell,
gently supported to the ground by the Tree-Tribe,
there was only a whispered groan
which emerged from its base-
a deep sigh of giving itself to Spirit.

All was well.

As tree spirit hovered over the men,
they chipped and hollowed out the core wood,
creating the craft for which the tree had grown.

They carefully shaped the front of the water-rider,
so that when it cut the water,
its movement would lift it
for easy resistance.

Its tapered shape,
would make the water pull at the back,
making the canoe move easily
with each cut of the paddles.

Each sleep they poured water into the opening
and heated smooth water-stones,
until they changed color.
Then they made the water bubble-hot.

It took three moons
to prepare Water-Rider.

But when it was done,
the forest grove and the young men
celebrated their sunset together.

They painted themselves and Tree-Tribe with red clay,
as a sign of long life and good medicine.

Other men,
who pulled canoes for the Tribe,
came to help get the craft down the mountain.

NADA

They initiated it by dipping it in the lake.

Then they placed it in the sun for curing
in bear and raccoon grease.
Rosen gums from spruce, fir, pine
and yellow cedar
were rubbed onto its outer surface.
Then it was washed with the men's urine.

At night, it took strength from our council fire spirit,
as it warmed over a trench of coals.
The sharp smell of hot rosin and sage smoke
helped prepare it for the Tribe.

By the Season-Of-Red-Leaves,
the spirits of the canoe and our Tribe were joined.

When the day was young
and the sky shined in the water,
Eagle Feather and Chief took the canoe to the lake,
where Great-Spirit received it
in a loon's fishing-call echo.

When its call went out of sound,
the men stepped in
to pull the canoe.
Chanting their canoeing song,
they dipped their paddles from side to side,
in rhythmic order.

Each noiseless stroke
moved them into gentle smoothness.

The paddle drips fell away
in easy ripple circles,
to become the silent lapping of the water
on the shore.

VII

MOON-SPIRIT'S-DAUGHTER

As daylight was getting old,
Moon-Spirit's-Daughter came to me
in a very shy manner.

Her way was quiet
and without words.
She had a heavy stomach.
This problem often happened
for women who worked with porcupine quills.

Moon-Spirit's-Daughter
had been ceremonially initiated
into the sacred art of quill work.

Many moons before
her first work had been presented to Sun.

Since then,
she had worked hard
at processing porcupine quills;
dying them in colored water,

wrapping them in a fawn's bladder
and sleeping on them at night
until they were ready;
softening the quills in her mouth
and flattening them between her teeth
for use in the quill designs,
for which she was well known.

I brewed some herbs
made of devil's club and fern roots.
She drank this for seven sleeps.

After taking a mint-water enema,
she ate roasted grubs and chekitas for a day.
I put warm, soft moss over her stomach,
and kept it warm with hot ashes from the fire.

Until the next moon,
she drank only spring water
and ate roasted chekita, fruits and vegetables.

The life-spirit of the vegetables
lightened her insides
and freed Vegetable-Spirits
to heal her stomach.

Once she was well,
her heart felt close to her chest,
and it seemed she was going to birth
as Spirit-Child messenger.

She felt full,
but no longer ill.

One night,
soon after this,
Moon-Spirits'-Daughter was awakened
by the silence of no leaves fluttering.

Not a wing of wind was moving.
Yet,
there were murmuring Mystery voices
in the silent night.

Sleep stopped pulling at her eyes.
She knew it was Great-Mystery
calling her to The-Wise-One's council.

Quietly getting up from her blanket,
she put it over her shoulders.
As she made her way in the grey-yellow moon light,
bats began sweeping the dark air.

Her feet lead her to Medicine-Lake.
There was no motion on its face.
Stars trembled overhead,
as if floating on an invisible surface.

She could see the top of sky-world.

A rhythmic beat came from deep inside the waters.
It was the heart of earth,
steady,
like the beating of her own heart;
each echoing the other.

They were one pounding throb.

From this untroubled place,
she was free to see outside
what she felt inside.

As she sat on her blanket,
close to the mothering power,
she felt the calmness of patience,
the wonder of reverence,
the dignity of being herself
and the courage of her endurance.

These were the direction-spirits
of her life.

In a lake side meadow,
under the quiet moving moon,
a band of deer came from the woods
and sported in a circle frolic-dance.

It continued
until Coyote's eerie voice talked to the moon.

Then there was silence everywhere;
so heavy, it smashed every noise.

NADA

This was Star-Nations silence.

They were moving evenly together,
as one mind.

Then the Extra-Ordinary-One showed her a vision.

It was a vision of the great circle,
the moon circle of growth;
the seasons which come back to where they start;
the round sun traveling in a circle;
and wind's whirl-power.

There was the circle of Eagle's nest
and the roundness of earth-sky.
In this great power,
all round things are relatives.

Standing in the middle of our circle,
the one thing we know is our power.

This is our life place.

And, so, we honor it
and live its contentment.

We are together-centered,
as one people.
This makes our union-power very strong.

We camp in a circle
and build our circle fires.

Our council fire shows our unity.
This is where we make our decisions
and our declarations.

When Moon-Spirit's-Daughter returned
and taught us about circle power,
we became a happy people.

Her moon path became our wisdom.
We learned how to live easy together.
We felt our belonging
in ways that words do not explain.

Our sign of peaceful power is our blanket.
It is our connection to earth-sky.
It is our place to belong.
It is our power.

VIII.

YELLOW-JACKET and COYOTE

Horn-Wing-Yellow-Jacket and Sly-Coyote
were out exploring Deer-Creek-Trail.

Otters were playing in the beaver pond
and raccoons were catching crayfish
under the rocks below the dam.

Birds were chirp-singing high overhead.
Fly-bugs filled the air with humming.

Everything seemed to be smooth with nature.
Everything,
that is,
except Coyote,
who had a twisted nose about himself.

Yellow-Jacket was giving him some unwanted advice.
  "Stay home.
  Keep yourself out of mischief.
  You always ask for trouble
  and set yourself up for difficulty."

"But what is life without
a little risk here and there?"
Coyote interrupted.
"Who always balances safety
on the end of their nose?
Only the fearful or the lame hearted.
I want a drink-full life;
no half-lapping swallows for me!
I live for the excitement of chase
and the adventure of exploring.
My word is:
'Do not turn from what makes you feel alive!'"

Yellow-Jacket grinned at Coyote's freedom desire,
for he too enjoyed taking risks.
"But,
I'm saying,
you put no wisdom behind your jumps
and no brains behind your actions.
You do,
then you pay attention."

Coyote's response was:
"He who thinks ahead
never jumps
and he who holds his choices in each paw
never walks.
All life is adventure,
so we can't out-grow doing!"

Yellow Jacket buzzed ahead on the trail,
"z-z-z-z-z-z-z…"

NADA

He was singing to himself,
for he thought Coyote was foolish.

Just as he got his stinger around the corner
he saw some of Coyote's favorite food
hanging in a bush-snare.

Anyone knows that long-eared-hoppers
do not hang in the high branches of a sagebrush.
That is,
unless they are blinded by stomach growling
and drooling mouth slobber.

So, Yellow-Jacket flew back to warn Coyote
that his freedom did not always come
by doing what he wanted.

He needed to look at some situations
with very suspicious eyes.

"Get out of my face!" Coyote snapped.
"I am tired of warnings and cautions."

"We shall see!"
Yellow-Jacket replied.
"For your test is just around the trail bend."

"Good!"
Retorted Coyote.

His mind went around the bend before him
and speeded up his run.
"Let's have a look!"

Together they rounded the rock pile.
Well!
When Coyote's nose caught the rabbit's smell,
he went crazy.

He sat for a bit
slurping air through his mouth
and drooling off the end of his tongue.

He was looking things over,
so he could spring just high enough to grab rabbit.

"Careful now!"
Hollered Yellow-Jacket
in Coyote's big ear.
*"Hold your feet with patience.
All is not by nature here.
When did you last see a hopper
hanging from a tree by his hind legs?"*

*"Sniff,
sniff,"*
Coyote went at the sagebrush roots.

The trail smelled clear.

NADA

By now his stomach was so loud,
that his mind was a closed as his eyes
when he was seven sleeps old.

He lunged for hopper
and sank his teeth in its white-grey fur.
As the weight of his body
tightened the snare around his neck,
he began to gasp for air.

Just as he was making his last twitch,
Yellow-Jacket swooped down
and stung him three or four times
on the end of his snout.

This made Coyote so mad,
he lunged for Yellow-Jacket.

His jump took pressure off the snare
and he caught an air-breath.
It also got the rope down farther on his chest
so that his pipes were not pinched closed.

Problem was,
he was held tall,
so that only his hind toenails scratched the ground.

Coyote squeezed out a gasp,
  "Get Cuts-Trees-With-His-Teeth.
  Have him chew on the sagebrush."

Off Yellow-Jacket flew
to awaken Cuts-Trees,
for he is a member of the night-Tribe.

He found him in the marsh,
working on his dam.

    "How can you ask me to do that?"
asked Long-Teeth.
      "It is such terrible, nasty tasting stuff.
      You expect me to chew!
      That's two days of hard work;
      and sagebrush!
      Puey!"

Yellow-Jacket knew Beaver had a soft heart,
and, finally, he got him to come cut on the sage.

Cuts-Trees started the undercut,
having to stop and spit every few chomps
to get rid of the nasty taste
that puckered up his lips.

Just as he was gagging from the juices,
Mask-Faced-Raccoon came along the trail,
swing his rump from side to side.

Yellow-Jacket asked him to climb the sage
and pull the boulder-stone off the snare
holding Coyote in the air.

NADA

As his fat body scrambled up the bush
it shook sage dust all over Cuts-Trees
who began sneezing,
  "A-choo! A-choo!"

Just then,
snare keeper came around the rock pile
and blew a stick through each animal.

It made Yellow-Jacket angry.
So, he stung the stick blower on the arm.

But he couldn't get his stinger out
and pulled himself apart
to die with his friends.

They all died,
and it was all because of Coyote's,
'I-don't-give-a-damn' attitude!

IX

PINK-ROSE'S THORN

Prairie-Grass was a noble woman,
who cooked the Tribal-Council's food.
She had tall-standing with us,
for she never talked what she heard.

Neither did she give away advice
based on wisdom she gained
from working with our Elders.

She never called attention to herself:
She walked simple and honest.
She was at home with herself.

But Pink-Rose was jealous
of Prairie-Grass' role,
and began to say unkind things
about this great woman.

Because Prairie-Grass was so respected,
Pink-Rose had to be very clever about all this.
She told of wonderful things
which everyone knew Prairie-Grass had done.

But in telling the great things,
she hid a rose thorn behind what she said.

She turned the stories
into painful hurt for Prairie-Grass.

They caused people to turn aside
and dislike this noble woman.

Realizing that this situation
had walked far down the stumbling trail,
Prairie-Grass came to me for advice.

I told her that whatever she did,
it was to be remembered
that we each reflect one another.

She would know what to do,
as she was self-respectful.

After our talk,
Prairie-Grass went to her humble lodge,
selected her most beautiful new dress
and, all her jewelry.

She took them directly to Pink-Rose's lodge
and called for her to come outside.

Pink-Rose was afraid
to face Prairie-Grass.

But this noble woman held strength-courage
in her heart,
and waited until Pink-Rose's friends came by.

With many friends to support her,
Pink-Rose finally came out of her lodge.

It was then
that Prairie-Grass put out her face before them,
and gave all her wealth to Pink-Rose.

She said simply:
  "Behold it in kindness."

She then turned and went back to her home,
having lived her self-respect.

In giving her inside peace,
she healed all hurt
and brought joy medicine to our Tribe.

She told me,
that by not holding judgment,
she let go of pain.

When Prairie-Grass gave everything to Pink-Rose,
it was a celebration of her freedom.

She was good to herself.

Not holding Pink-Rose to her past,
Prairie-Grass could live in peace with the present.

X.

ROLLING-BIG-THUNDER

No one knew Rolling-Big-Thunder's mother or father.
He was a gift from Spirit.
This is how it happened:

One day,
during a storm,
I heard a new-born crying outside my teepee flap.

I took the little one,
who still grew his birth cord,
and held him to the seven directions:
The-Sun-Of-New-Life-And-Light,
The-Land-Of-Sun-And-Warmth,
The-Land-Of-Setting-Sun,
The-Land-Of-The-Bite-Wind,
up to the above-sky
and down to the below-earth,
finally,
to the silent-quiet inside myself.

The fire from my heart covered the boy
with All-Mother's power.

There was no sky-sun,
So, I held him toward Lightning-Chief.
He was a child of Sky-Spirit;
now born of earth.

I named him
"Rolling-Big-Thunder,"
and prayed:
  "Ho!
  All that moves in the sky-air,
  new life has come to us.
  Behold hills, valley, and rivers.

  Here is Rolling-Big-Thunder.

  Birds, animals and insects,
  see this child through life.

  Let Rolling-Big-Thunder
  be gladly good hearted,
  and his mind be made of kind thoughts.

  May he seek a purity-vision,
  and be renewed for medicine power."

Suddenly sky lightning flashed,
storm Spirits sang wild songs,
and the air was full of mystery.

There were no more words.

Rolling-Big-Thunder's traditional clay bowl,
given to him at birth
(to be broken at his death),
was filled with rain water.

Silently,
I took the liver of a new killed pheasant
and rubbed it on Rolling-Big-Thunder's forehead
for patient understanding.

I put chipmunk oil on his feet
for caution-speed on the trail,
and bees honey on his hands
for hard work for the Tribe.

Then I took little limbs of sage brush
and made a wreath for his head
and bands for his wrists and ankles.

For Rolling-Big-Thunder to learn nature's lessons
and grow to provide a good life for all,
I asked Gray-Wolf,
our village scout,
to stretch and grow the child strong.

Gray-Wolf was like a lone pine
standing tall in the forest.
Rolling-Big-Thunder was a little tree
growing in the forest shade.
Both had big powers for Spirit.

So,
from his beginning-life,
Rolling-Big-Thunder was on the trails
with Gray-Wolf.

A lean-to in Elk-Forest
was home for them.
They stayed outside for all the seasons,
like the thunder.

They ate only before sun rise and after sun set.

Each held his silence,
for Gray-Wolf believed that action
was the only way to talk.

    "Words kill thought."
    He said.
    "Explanations cover up knowing.
    Words hide our open experience of life."

Rolling-Big-Thunder's keen eye
put everything on a good memory.

His powers were strong
to see and find what no one else could.
No leaf motion missed his watchful eye.

His understanding was deep.

He tracked all kinds of animals
and learned how to be drawn into their strength.
Their tracks told their story,
and they trusted his footsteps.

He gave up his thoughts
so they could meet
at the place for sharing their lives.

He never named what he was to meet,
for naming them would make them decide to live
instead of giving him their death.

He and the animals shared everything together.
As he opened himself to them,
each one became his Mystery-guide.

Rolling-Big-Thunder grew to know
the small details and wisdom
of the ones he followed.

He learned to receive protection
from these friends and teachers,
and he listened to their warnings.

They became together-life,
helping and honoring one another.

Gray-Wolf and he walked with the moose
in frog swamps.
They called the calf and mother
with special birch whistles.

They followed easy-foot cats
and saw how they cared for their young.

They watched how the tumble-bug beetles,
stood on buffalo droppings
and pointed their horns
toward the grazing herd.

They watched wolves,
and studied them
when they were alone or in a pack.

They dropped stones in front of bear caves
and saw how the mother came to listen
and then to stand on her hind legs outside the den.

He learned the ways of squirrels and raccoons.

In the forest, he knew himself.

They stayed outside during all the seasons,
like the thunder.

Very early, Rolling-Big-Thunder had a dream-dance,
helping him to get courage and special help.
He was initiated young
with secret ceremonies.

He received a special turtle-shell rattle,
a buffalo blow-horn,
and a shield made of mountain sheep hide,
as signs of his medicine powers.

NADA

His moccasins were quill beaded
and his leggings were made of mountain goat wool.

In his medicine bag
was a curved rabbit stick for throwing.
It brought any spiritual presence
back to where he stood.

He also learned
to make stone hunting and fishing tools.

These gifts were especially for him,
and not any other child in the Tribe.

In learning to become a tribal scout,
he examined every animal's print.
He could tell when they passed,
their weight,
what sex,
their age,
and where they were likely to be.

His glance saw every movement and life-sign,
as if they were forever fixed.

He observed the trampled grass
or the bent limb,
the broken twig
or any slight change along the trail.

He studied every object for its disturbances.

Every sound,
not matter how small,
had meaning.
Every sound was Spirit's talk.

Small changes in the actions of animals or birds
told many stories and held many lessons.

The circles of soaring buzzards
signaled something to be checked out.

Crane calls spoke of the coming weather.

Frogs,
singing with ancient voices,
let him know of hidden springs.

He was guided by the animal's ways.
Nature yanked at his Spirit
and become his wisdom.

He developed a care for all her Tribes.
He learned their languages.
He could talk with them
more easily than with a person.

Together,
they shared Movement-With-All-Life.

He also learned from Gray-Wolf how to fish,
when to use the spear,
when to use a woven willow trap,
when to shoot with an arrow,
when to use the cucumber vine to stun them,
and how to tease them with a stick
so that they came to the pond surface.

They netted or speared the salmon,
depending on the water.
Often, he would water-wiggle his hand
so the salmon would come directly to it,
as if it were the shadow of a spawning fish.

They smoked and dried their catch
or baked them in the white ashes of the camp fire.
Fishing lessons were not simply how to fish,
they were an understanding
of fish and water ways.

They were lessons on being himself.

He learned how riffles settled the sand
and how rocks made the water's flow.
He learned about trick-images under the top-waters.

Most of all,
he learned to think and swim like a fish
and to understand the stream Spirit.

He learned the fish ceremonies and traditions.
When he caught the first salmon of the season,
he circled his camp with it,
gave it a kiss
and returned it to the water
with its head facing upstream.

Then he would sing:
> *"Remember us honorable Salmon.*
> *Return home and tell your people;*
> *I went to The-People-Camp*
> *and they treated me well.*
>
> *They showed respect.*
>
> *We must return to them*
> *so they will have food."*

As a final comment,
he would say to Great-Mystery-Power,
> *"Keep bad luck from the Salmon."*

In hunting deer,
he learned how to aim his arrows
if the animal was running or standing still,
when it was far away or close by,
when it was day or night.

He learned how they would move and act.
He would wait and move
in the patterns of forest darkness,
following them
so the course of their actions
would make their final meeting
a journey of magic and honor.

In the drifting white-crystals
he would short-chase them
before they got winded.

But just after having young,
their hides were thin and their meat was tough.

Near mating-season they were fat
and their meat was tasty.

The methods of deer hunting were as many as fishing.

If trail snares were set,
the deer had to be chased into them.
If the deer was trail or lake ambushed,
when they came to eat or drink,
Rolling Big Thunder used spears rather than arrows.

Usually,
he fixed his mind in prayer
and drew the animals to him.

It was a silent song,
where the animals accepted
the sacred favor of Change-Being.
They received new life through death.
They became new creatures.

Because Rolling-Big-Thunder honored them with respect,
they could return to their Spirit homes
and be re-born to help The-People-Tribe.

With a large grass straw
Rolling-Big-Thunder learned to make chipmunk noises.

During The-Season-Of-Green-Grass,
when they came out of their ground holes
through the white blanket,
he could get them to gather around in big numbers.
He learned to whistle bird songs,
and they came to him in large flocks.

Animal sounds became his other voice
and he spoke with each one in its own language.

If the animals he saw
were from the prairie
rather than woodland or forest,
Rolling-Big-Thunder observed them in their home range.

He knew all the rock formations and the wallows,
the salt licks and the watering holes.

He could stampede the buffalo over a steep cliff
and use a large stone skull cracker or lance
to kill them.

He could ambush them
and with his bow bent full draw,
he could twang an arrow under their ribs
and through their hearts.

If they were running,
he would sometimes drive his arrow
into the rear hip joint.
Once the animal sat down,
an arrow or lance could be thrown through its heart.

This was especially necessary,
if the chase would be long,
for when animals run far
their meat is hard to chew.

Rolling-Big-Thunder's bow and arrow
were part of him.
They sang together as one voice.

Gray-Wolf had taught him
to make his arrows from straight serviceberry branches
and attach eagle and humming bird wing feathers.
to air guide them.

Once Rolling-Big-Thunder could bend a bow
to match the young moon's curve,
Gray-Wolf taught him to make strong, singing bows
from choke-cherry,
red cedar
and fire hardened yew wood.

Then he gave them to the strength of the animals
they were to kill.

He wrapped his bows in buffalo sinew
and rattlesnake skin.
They were held together with glue
made by boiling buffalo siring rods.

Rolling-Big-Thunder could shoot without aim
and strike his target with ease.

By bending the bow only within his reach,
he put power into his arrow.
It traveled far with much force.

Often his arrows
went completely through the animals he shot.
He sent his energy to the animal,
so that in its death
their spirits met together.

Every movement was an act of holy obedience.
The animal's death became their shared gift
of reverence and respect,
teaching him his place in mystery life.

To the animal,
it was the path to Change-Being.
So the death arrow was received with thanksgiving.

Another way Gray-Wolf taught Rolling-Big-Thunder
to show respect and care for the animals,
was to celebrate our traditional rituals
and see life in a sacred way.

He taught Rolling-Big-Thunder
to take painted holy sticks from his bundle,
place them in the ground beside the fire
and to watch the wind blow the eagle feather plumes,
as signs of blessing in the hunt.

It was the assurance of food and clothes.

In silence,
he would walk in the way his prayer plumes showed,
and talk with the animal's spirit.

Then he cam back to the campfire,
drew the animal's picture in the sand
and invited its spirit to join him.

Together they put a log on the fire
symbolizing the animal's body.
He would then blow on the coals
to make the log burn.

In this way,
he blew hunting power
into the animal's life.
He put before the fire,
his eagle wing medicine whistle,
flint charms and wolf stone.

These charms represented his power animals.
After putting sand-circles around each power object,
he sang and danced
to the animal spirits
who came to their fire.

These rituals honored his connection with them.
They were a sacred preparation
for receiving the animal's power-fertility,
and the lessons they would bring.

When the Spirit arrived,
and told him of the hunt,
Rolling-Big-Thunder sang to the earth directions:
    "The Spirit has come,
    hi-hi-wa-hi!
    hi-hi-wa-hi!
    hi-hi-wa-hi!
    hi-hi-wa-hi!"

Once the animal was killed,
he took a cedar branch
and brushed its cloud-spirit robe.

Then with a hollow eagle bone,
he blew yellow cancer-root pollen
into the animal's mouth
and toward the campfire,
where the animal's spirit was a guest.

Once the animal's head was toward camp,
Rolling-Big-Thunder's flint knife opened its throat.
Its blood poured out onto the earth,
as he reverently chanted:
    "O Earth.
    Drink.
    It belongs to you."

Then he cut inside.
Parts of the spleen and liver
were given to Crow-Tribe,
as a thank-gift.

The brains were saved
to be mixed with the animal's fat,
for curing the hide.
He ate part of the raw liver.

Blood from the cavity
was scooped into a shallow hole,
dug beside the animal,
so that earth was fed again.

Evergreen branches were laid beside the animal,
so that blood stayed off the hide
and dirt stayed off the meat.

While cutting the meat
and cleaning out the insides,
Gray-Wolf taught Rolling-Big-Thunder
to talk to the animal's spirit
as to a friend.

They were messengers of holy calling.
The animal spirits
would speak through him
and sing the mystery of each life.

Because of his reverence and respect,
their lives continued in him.

Rolling-Big-Thunder became very courageous
and nature let him handle vicious animals.

They understood the silence of his quiet mind
and gave him their lives.
His power animals were faithful to him,
so he was not able to be destroyed by any animals,
no matter how ferocious.

He learned to silently accept every challenge
with stubborn toughness,
and to endure hardship
while listening with an open heart,
to the lessons of Mystery.

He learned to dance to the earth's drum beat
and could not be destroyed.

NADA

He understood how to travel in dream-visions
without losing his way.

He listened to the inside power,
which knew what he did not know.

Because the power of his animal teachers,
would enter his awakened thoughts,
he would run for days without stopping.

His pathless journeys were a big challenge.

His big joy was catching eagles.

They were his way in The-Blue-Spirit-Trail
and always carried good medicine for him.

After fasting,
he would climb to the base of high cliffs
where the power-stones were strong,
and dig a deep hole
in the directions which sun sky-traveled.

Over this he stretched an old deer hide.
Then he covered it with Manzanita brush.
In the darkness before dawn,
he would go to the covered hole
and put rock rabbit bait on top,
while he hid under the brush.

Because sometimes bears or wolves
came for the bait,
he had to sing an eagle song.

It took great patience to wait
until the magpies and crows arrived to test the bait.

Once the eagles saw the other birds,
they would land nearby to check everything for
themselves.

Then, with eagles on the bait,
he would slowly reach up between the branches
and carefully catch their feet.
After bringing them into the hole,
he would break their necks.

This slow, gentle action
released their medicine power to Rolling-Big-Thunder.

This helped him walk the sky pathways
knowing that he held,
within himself,
part of all living things.

Before skinning the birds,
he held them in each of the directions.
After making circle motions with the sweet grass,
he put incense over each eagle
for purification.

At the close of the day,
he would sing to the eagles,
   "Good-Eagle,
   and all your children,
   thank you for wealth and health."

He used the eagle wing-tip feathers
for seeking Spirit guidance.

The next largest feathers were used for fans
at healing ceremonies.

The breast plumes,
from over the heart,
were prayer decorations,
for new dancers or initiates
who needed eagle power,
or for throwing to the clouds when asking for rain.

The skull was used for wisdom ceremonies.

None of this great bird was thrown aside.

When the air grew too heavy
for Rolling-Big-Thunder to lift it to his mouth,
he gave his body to Earth-Mother.

His bones were used for magic power.

His Spirit went into The-Big-Thunder-Mountains,
where storms are the feathers of his bonnet,
even to this day.

XI

GENTLE-ONES of PEACEFUL-PRESENCE

Late one evening
I was standing beside by the lake.
I had the feeling I should invite Wind
to blow a strong breath across the water.

Someone needed to come ashore.

I danced
and threw my voice to the wind.

The bitten moon was standing high,
so I could only faintly see a square raft
floating toward me.

What a joy-surprise to find Little-Coyote
lying asleep on the reed raft.

When I awakened him,
he said he knew I would bring him home,
so, he had gone to sleep.

He told me that Old-Cedar and he had taken a trip.

He asked if what Cedar had told him was true.

Even before hearing his story,
I told him that whether it happened so or not,
it was true,
for it meant more than we understood.

Then Little-Coyote told me what had happened.

It seems that one day Old-Cedar,
Whose hair had turned white as the Bite-Wind's dawn
and whose body was bent like timberline pines
after many cold seasons,
was watching the sun
draw dancing spirits from the earth.
　　"They are doing a shimmer dance."
He told Little-Coyote.
　　"See them out there on the land edge,
　　where Sun speaks hot to Earth?"

Little-Coyote laughed
because the old one's voice
sounded like two trees rubbing together
when a gentle wind blows in the forest.

　　"Where else do they dance?"
He asked.

Old-Cedar quietly said:
  "Our holy ones dance
  when mists rise from the lake,
  or when a wind stirs the leaves.

  They travel on sunbeams
  and ride on lightning.

  They cross over rainbows
  and dance with the rain.

  On cold nights, you hear them
  singing in the green wood,
  as it burns on the fire.

  Sometimes you see them jump bright
  in the flames.

  You can see their footprints
  on the star trail of the sleeping sky.

  Like the day stars,
  they are there whether you see them or not."

This was more than Little-Coyote wanted to think.

Just then he got a tickle on his arm
and began to scratch.

"Ah-Ha!"
Shouted Cedar,
"A tickle is a touch,
honoring you with Ancestor nearness."

Little-Coyote doubt-wrinkled his nose,
so, Old-Cedar took him on his knee saying:
"Come.
Let me tell you about our holy ones,
whose teepee is the sky.

Once the wind was so cold
my breath clouds became hard drops on my head furs.

I was fishing through a clear lake skin,
thinking old dreams of what my life was to be.

Suddenly my feet slipped into the fishing hole,
tearing the hide which lake was wearing.

I dropped into the sluggish, heavy water.
This is very dangerous.
Because water does not like to be disturbed
when it is sleeping.

Like a surprised animal,
it tried to kill me.

I could not feel my feet after two eye blinks.
I pushed on the lake's hard cover
by lunging at it like a frightened wolf,
fighting for its life.

But the long ice-stabbers,
hanging under it into the lake,
kept breaking and rattling like dry bones.

As the clear robe split away from me,
I began to lose strength.

I heard Death-Wind call,
like a nightmare bringer.

But I said I would not listen.

So, I sang my magic song.
The Wise-Men taught it to me
when I was your sky-tallness.
'Sky-Force is mine today.
Earth and water run away.
The sun and moon are mine to play.
The seasons must obey.'

Suddenly,
I was standing on flat-water-land.

The Wise-One was beside me.
Then he quietly walked away,
without leaving any moccasin prints.

As the water began to make a clear cover
on my buffalo skin,
I asked for walking power
to face the winds.

NADA

I ran to Medicine-Man,
for herbs to unfreeze my spirit blanket.
We burned red cedar to the Wise-One,
who had saved my life.

Another time,
I was walking alone in the open,
under the blue sky
beside Fish-Lake.

I came to a rock slide-pile beside the trail.
A large rock came loose
and the hillside began moving toward me.

I ran.

But big rocks began falling
like grasshoppers jumping in the sky.
I couldn't get into the lake,
because it was too far from the trail.

Just then,
a great stone stopped beside me.
While I stood behind it,
the moving stones went around its edge.
Where they met again,
they buried past my knees.
When the rock shift was over,
I could not move.

FACE-OF-THE-RISING-SUN

I unburied my legs
as far as I could lift stones out of the hole.
Through my moccasins
I could feel that my toes were on my feet top.

I could not move.

Night was creeping down the trail toward me.
I heard the coyotes
talking about my being caught
in the mountain snare.

> *'Hoo-u,*
> *Hoo-u,*
> *Hoo-u!'*
In their echo calls,
I also heard Destroyer singing his song.

I knew that our Ancestors were leaning close to earth,
so, I said to Moon-Spirit:
> *'That song is for another brother!*
> *Maker, Holder and Preserver of my life,*
> *help me now!'*

In the white haze dusk,
my father stood beside me.

Two seasons before,
he had walked into the woods
for his last journey.

He never said a word.
And without moving a stone,
he lifted me out of the stuck-rocks.

He left like a flame goes out in the wind.

My mouth tasted like a crow's nest.
I was happy to be alive
and my joy shot up
like fire sparks on a dark windless night.

The Star-Nation hid themselves in daylight
four times before I crawled into camp.

Fly-worms were eating the green slime from my feet.
Later my toes dropped off.

I learned to walk again.

My life is many times thankful to my father.

I know he is looking after me
in case I need him again,
for Ancestor power is like that."

"What about the stone
which stood beside the trail?"
Little Coyote asked.

Old-Cedar smiled reverently.
"I go there often
to say thanks to the Sacred-One.

Wind worn and rain washed,
it speaks to me in silence.

It speaks of Great-Mystery
whose action is nature,
and whose power is in the sun."

"How do you hear,
if it speaks in silence?"
Little-Coyote asked.

"What is unspoken,
calls for us to listen.

This is a language heard
only by those for whom it is meant.

These are sacred heart beats.

Land is our trainer.
Sun is our guide.
The forest paths teach our feet to walk
but the dust of our Ancestors
become the whisper in our ears.

To be sure of ourselves,
silence must rule our lives."

"Take me to the mystery rock."
Little-Coyote requested.

"Prepare yourself.

NADA

We shall cross the lake
as dawn walks down the path
before the rising sun;
when the quiet rhythms
brush against your cheeks."

In the darkness before dawn,
while the sky stars and the water stars
looked the same at each other,
Old-Cedar waited on the reed raft.

He had a handful of dried salal berries,
acorn bread and dried salmon,
wrapped in a cedar bark basket,
as a gift for the Supernatural.

From the long mists in the dark woods,
a gentle song air-floated onto the lake.

The sky
shining itself in the lake,
silently carried them along.

Sun rise was simple and clear.
Its circle of power-strength
flashed in the lake.

When the sunbeams' slant
was the same as the paddle handles' slant,
a mysterious power pulled the raft across the water.

It was drawing at Old-Cedar's chest
and he was singing:
  "Oh, Mysterious Sun,
  we breath the air with you.
  We see your water smile.
  We trust your way upon the land."

When they reached shore,
the great trail-stone was waiting for them.

Little-Coyote stayed
while Old-Cedar went by himself
to his sacred place.

Using embers gathered from the village fire,
Old-Cedar lit green tree limbs.
its incense-smoke filled the air.

Little-Coyote heard Cedar chanting:
  "This spot is a holy spot.
  This spot is a holy place."

When Little-Coyote reached the fire,
Old-Cedar had climbed the smoke and was gone.

There was a new painted rock-stripe,
under which an offering of salal berries
was being eaten by Blue-Jay.

The gift-spirit had been received by Sun.

Little-Coyote sat down.
His thought shook in his head
like gourd seeds in a rattle.

Then he heard Blue-Jay sing:
  "Hear us of Sun!
  Let Old-Cedar walk safely,
  as he goes far.

  Help him complete the life trail.

  He is through with his initiation.

  He has walked the good trail
  to his quiet day.

  Let the wind,
  which gave his beginning-breath,
  receive his last sigh."

When Blue-Jay disappeared,
silence was heavy with Mystery.

It was strong
and held our Ancestors' heart secrets.

Little-Coyote never saw Old-Cedar again.

But he often felt him near
and would sometimes call him
to come back from the other side.

During these times,
he would go to the lake,
break limbs from the sacred tree,
and cleanse his body
by slapping himself with the wet branches.

This cleansing always brought a healing that said:
"Till we meet at dawn."

XII.

SUN-DANCE AND
HIS POWER-VISION

One of the most handsome young men in the Tribe
came to my lodge.
This same season before,
he had returned from a successful Vision-Quest.
Now he wanted to go on another.

He said Spirit was calling him
for the good of our Tribe.

Sitting before the center hole of my teepee,
I gave Sun-Dance eagle feathers for his hair.
They were to help his thoughts rise high,
like the eagles.

With sacred cedar bark,
I put white paint and deer fat
over his body.

Then he joined me
in an ancient ritual.
The walk of his song was:

"From the place of beginnings,
   I come.
(Emerging from the central hole,
he danced around the sacred teepee.)
   I will travel
   by holy trails into the unknown."
From one side of the teepee to the other,

I laid down sacred meal and pollen powder,
as a life line.
   "I bring
   the sacred life-flame,
   which burns inside me now."

From the fire,
he removed a long stick,
burning at one end.
   "Holding in my hands this great power,
   I draw it into my body.
   I am Spirit's action."
He did a fire dance
with the flaming torch.
   "I remember my animal medicine,
   for supernatural power."
He threw bear skins off his body.

I sit quietly
in the center
where the power of all directions
over cross each other.

NADA

I wait for Spirit to speak my name.

He sat naked,
breathing from the palm of his open hand.

I painted the sign of morning star on his forehead,
and a butterfly on his back.

I gave two instructions:
  "As you face the winds,
  be strong and pure.

  Face the round morning sun
  with prayers of thanks."

I sent my voice to the directions:
  "Hey-a-a-hey!
  Hey-a-a-hey!
  Hey-a-a-hey!
  Hey-a-a-hey!"

Feeling the spiritual confirmation for his Quest,
I sent him away on his solitude-journey
with songs, dances and prayers;
acts of hope for spiritual powers.

He left my lodge,
and went to a willow thicket,
on the far side of the lake.

He sat naked,
in the reflected silver-gray lake dawn.

As Rabbit was eating shore-line cowslips,
Sun-Dance was thoughtful
about his new power demonstration.

He had already given himself to danger
and achieved high honor
for his bravery and strong endurance.

On this Vision-Quest,
he was to obtain skills
from his animal guides.
He was to build a better life for our people.

He had already met his bear power
and received her power song.
Now he was being sent out,
as a male during the breeding cycle.

Across Medicine-Lake,
the Council Fires grew pale.
Dawn drifted away
on clouds upon the wind.

Smoke emerged in thin blue coils
from many lodge fires.

It was time for him to let the outside go
and to enter the inside silence.

He prayed for peace, harmony and strength.
In the magical light,
as Great-Star arose from the sky-land,

he thought of his 'Mother's Child' moons.

When his mother had given him flesh and blood,
in a mosey glen close to where he now sat,
she had prepared a honeysuckle-vine nest.

She had placed him in this cradle,
where the smell of moss mulch and flower blossoms
celebrated his earth ties.

He was declared:
> *"Son-Of-Great-Spirit,*
> *Holy-One-Of-Earth*
> '*' "

being a name only he, I and his parents knew.
No one gives away their sacred name.

His visitors had been an eagle,
who carried away
the things which tied him inside his mother;
a she-wolf,
who licked him clean;
and a rattle snake,
who moved its tail for his enjoyment.

From then,
until his first Vision-Quest,
he had run free through the meadows,
along forest paths,
and beside the lake.

He had grass-wind danced with camus blossoms,
paint brushes
and sunflowers.

Buffalo herds ignored him
and coyotes sat to watch him
jump through the tall grass.

Out by the rosebushes,
while eating rose hips,
he had watched a prairie dog call to a passing hawk.

It was his final walk.

This memory brought a shiver-jerk.

He realized that this Quest
was the same as prairie dog's.

Just then blackbird landed on his canoe and said:
> *"The wind that rustles in the reeds*
> *and stirs the ripple-water,*
> *is the guide which you must know.*

> *It is the breath of Mother's life.*

> *And in the silent shadows*
> *she whispers now to you.*

> *Listen,*
> *but do not speak!*

Hidden in the meadow grass,
you learned of fox and coyote.
In the forest wisdom was wolf and owl.

On the lake,
the laughter of the loon.

But now,
when you hear the wind,
it is a message just for you.

Listen.
But do not speak!"

He moved his eyes to the ground,
put his hand before his face,
palm in,
breathed deeply of Spirit;
in-taking life-breath.

After getting to his feet,
he drew his foot backward.
His big toe made a ripple in the sand.

A blue needle-fly landed on the ripple.

Then he entered the tall tree shadows.
It was his entrance into Mystery.

On his way through yellow-pine forest
he sat to rest on a large round rock,
and remembered a cradle song
his mother had dream-learned
just before he was born.

In the pine shadows,
the memory of her voice met his silence:
"Come little one,
sit upon the earth.
Let her warmth become your rest.

Feel her touch,
as she holds you near
in moonlight's joy.

Receive her life.
Listen as she sings.
It is your dream-song."

These words brought courage
and he chanted them to himself.

He was beginning another life,
a life to fulfill his first moons.

He was sent here,
alone,
to learn wisdom.

NADA

This was his spirit walk,
the path which was his travel with All.

He must now listen to the living stones,
the breathing mountains
and the walking rain.

As he kicked a stone across the path
he noticed a little stream singing alone.

He water drank
from the cup of his hand.
Then he blew a spraying mist prayer
from his mouth.

It was a power song.
The words remembered themselves to him:
  "Nestle in the laughing brook.
  Feel the joy of pollywogs at play.

  Hear the clatter of the stones
  as they wash and roll today.

  Enjoy the wonder of it all,
  for its magic is your way."

He turned deeper into the woods,
and had a strong sense of the Mysterious.

He heard another song:
    "Accept the wind's embrace
    and you will find the wonder of its grace.
    Hear it tumble through the leaves
    upon the forest floor.
    It plays the frolic of a fawn.

    Feel the freedom of the blowing leaf
    that lights upon the moss,
    and shifts to find its place
    upon the earth which calls it home.

    It has known the forest grandeur
    and fulfilled itself upon the tree.
    Now it shares itself with earth
    from which it came."

Watching the squirrels
gathering acorns and pine nuts,
and digging away the tree roots,
helped him laugh
at how the frogs were croaking in his stomach.

He wondered how it would be
when he reached Standing-Bear-Mountain
to begin fasting and prayers,
as preparation for his Vision-Dreams.

He had to become pure,
so he could help others
on their way to spiritual power.

After wandering four lonely suns,
he came to Standing-Bear-Mountain,
and the holy rocks
through which spirit-wind whispered.

Rain was spilling clouds.
Again, a song walked through his mind
He called it: "Come feel the rain."
    "Dawn awakened you today,
    and now would bath you
    in the water-spilling sky.

    In the washing of your skin,
    you learn what makes the flowers grow
    and rivers run so free.

    Come feel the rain.
    Come feel the rain."

When he reached the mountain top
he reverently walked to a tree
which had known many moons of sky secrets.

He felt the strong medicine of Great-Spirit.
It crawled into his blood.

His first sleep was under the eagle's nest;
he curled into the same position
the eagle had found him as a baby.

On awakening,
she asked him what he had seen.
    "Night lights dancing the sky.
    They left,
    so stars could bring the day."

    "Ah!
    You are blind!"
She called as she flew away.

He watched her high-wind circle tracks,
calling his dreams to the sky.

On the edge of sight,
he felt empty sky power.
Flapping his arms like a fledgling,
he chanted over and over:
    "O Light,
    become my view.
    O Light,
    become my view."

He did not remember stopping,
but as eagle sat on the nest logs beside him
she began a dance
-a prayer of sort's
-a trail through his blind darkness;
teaching him the heart way
and its language.
    "You have seen only your own light.
    You have never gone beyond your shadow.

NADA

He felt like a fish,
when the talons spear its sides,
dragging it into the air.
The he felt the smashing of his head!

He must get past his mind-thoughts,
whose noise stopped him from hearing Spirit.

His thoughts were as many as the stars.
He longed for silence and the light-vision.

Eagle's dance continued.
  *"See from your heart.
  This is your only light."*

  "But for what do I look?"
Sun-Dance's voice shook the nest as an earth shift.

Again, eagle flew away.
When she returned
she brought a fawn's heart for him to eat.

As he ate,
the little creature jumped from his mind
and into the meadows;
a reminder of Great-Spirit's heart-space.
It shared its soul-breath with him
and gave its body for his vision.
He became the fawn.

Theirs was one sacred power
-One life-bringer.
-One way of shared mystery.

Eagle's dance continued.
　"You are All.
　Look!
　You shall see."

He looked to where rustling cottonwood trees grew
among the river brush sticks,
and watched the bird songs air-climb.

He saw the long prairie grass and flowering plants
waving in the breeze.
Among the spear leafed pines
he followed trails,
where boulder monuments caught the sky.

Eagle's dance continued.

As he opened himself
to the One-Who-Moves-In-All-Things,
he received his sacred purification.

He sat silently.
Waiting.
Listening for the inside word,
which would slash open his body
and set his Spirit free.

He was hungry for full cleansing.

As he sat there,
a song played deep within:
    "Accept the wind's embrace
    and you will find its grace.

    The wind that rustles in the reeds
    and stirs the water into ripples,
    is the guide that you must know.

    Feel the blowing leaf-freedom,
    which finds its place
    upon the earth which calls it home."

As Eagle waited,
his wind flight began to change.

An unseen force wrapped around Sun-Dance,
and took hold of his Spirit.
Lift-Mysterious breathed the directions
into his nostrils.

It threw him from the nest.
It wrestled him to the ground.

All fight was gone.
All resistance flew away.

His hand was broken by the fall,
and with each blood spurt,
he felt his life returning to Earth-Mother.

Would his dream die upon the blood-red ground?

His thoughts were like smoke signals,
which spread and go into the sky.

He lay there half awake.
His Power-Quest was all that stayed.
He had a deep longing to be united with Spirit.

Blue flamed Thunder-People danced all around him.
Fire Spirits,
every one!

His first journey lived again:
When he walked up the mountain before,
almost like another life,
he had gone through the discipline;
the sacrificial rituals
and the ceremonies.

He had demonstrated courage and self control.
He had swept his inside lodge clean
and was fully alive.

Even though young with hope,
the Mind-Of-Mountain had entered inside.

NADA

With his own hand lance
he had killed the grizzly bear:
his power animal.

As a holy journey
he had followed her tracks
and those of her yearling cubs.
They had led him to the cave
whose mouth was covered with serviceberry bushes.

He had dropped his blanket before their den.

When she stood upright to offer herself,
they had stood in each other's presence
with strong honor.
He had sent the death wound directly to her heart.

She had fallen where he now lay:
Her valiant spirit still inside.
It was this life they now shared:
A life that had made him new.

Now he could feel the breath of her cub
and his life-circle was closing.

He met the drum beat of his life.

Everything was uncertain.

What had he done with his brave valor?
(where was) the heart that swelled in his chest
when Chief wore the bear claws,
so that when he walked,
they rattled like a running grizzly?

The Chief had sat upon her fur
while holding Tribal Council.

Where was his thanksgiving to the grizzly,
now standing over him,
whose mother had blessed his people?
How could he represent his people now?

Hunt as he might,
he found neither shame nor pride;
neither a desire to live or to die.

Nor did he find a difference between himself
and the young grizzly standing over him.

Their strength-power flowed pure and clear;
like a stream.
It was a single life-
alive!
He had lived his story.

When he awakened,
his before moons ran away.

Bear had gnawed off his hand;
a gesture which saved his life,
for it stopped the blood spurts
of his beating heart.

Wolf was licking his wounds.
She nuzzled his body and gave him strength-milk.

By dusk,
he and wolf crawled together to a water pool,
where silver falls-spray gently brushed him
with leaf-like hands.

The embracing water brought feelings of affection.
It was unclear how long he rested in the mist-water.
But he and wolf were awakened
by the hot noon-day's sun.
She nursed him,
licked his healing wounds,
and left,
to care for her young.

He spent four sleeps beside the falling water.

He watched Bear and Mountain-Cat come,
bow
and drink.

He saw how the easy change-water,
and its gentle push,
wore away the stones
and opened up the earth.

This too was his power!

Even in his weakness,
he climbed to the Sacred-Rocks
on the mountain top.

To his surprise,
there stood the giant animal
for which his father was named:
Great-Black-Headed-Elk.

He had tangled his antlers with a whistler bull.
Together they had led the herd
to these high mountain pastures.

Life had already left the other animal.
Chief-Of-The-Elk-Tribe was down;
his powers almost gone.

The words out of Sun-Dance's mouth were:
"Limitation is but a trail to freedom."

'*What foolishness!*'
He scolded himself,
as he ran to the spring
to get water for the Chief.

Gourds were the only containers he found.
He filled them with water
and hobble-ran back to the great animal.

NADA

The water stayed in Chief's throat
and made his struggle end.

But Elk-Spirit stayed with Sun-Dance,
for only the greatest of all hunters
can kill The-Chief-Of-The-Mountain-Plains
and have its soul remain.

Through his purification tears,
he scraped and dressed the hide.

Then for many sleeps he lay on the skin without food.

When his thoughts came back,
a rattle-tailed serpent rested beside him.
Taking it in his one remaining hand,
he raised snake to the sky
and sent his voice,
saying:

    "Spirit of the Earth.
    Behold.
    I am the Sun.
    Behold.
    I am the Sun.
    A-hey!
    A-hey!
    A-hey!
    A-hey!"

Like sacred arrows sky falling,
six star-people were beside him,
holding council on the elk hide.

    "Laputi,"
    they called him.
    "Laputi,
    this life is yours to make.
    These are your heart words."

    "There is in me the power.
    Earth is my spirit alive,"
    replied, now, Laputi

As suddenly as The-Star-Nation had come,
they moved out of sight
between the open edges of the sky.

As they passed the high bluffs,
they picture wrote a promise.

The picture said
that they would meet him here each cycle
of his spiritual retreat,
and would lead him through the season.

Great-Sun declared:
    "I take Laputi for my friend.
    May we meet and be happy again.

    Ho-ho-ho-HOH,
    He-he-he-HEE-YAH."

419

As a sacred symbol,
the Star-Nation people
left him a round, blue stone
to put with his string of elk teeth.
This was his supernatural medicine.

His bravery song was:
"There is in me the power.
There is in me the power.
Ho-ho-ho-HOH,
He-he-he-HEE-YAH."

When he arrived at camp,
the day was old and wise.
I met him.

Laputi was singing:
"I am a man.
I am a man."

He was brave to sing this song,
for it meant he had the courage to dare,
the power to stand,
and the strength to endure.

He could claim to be a man.

He had set his mark
and others would be guided by his deeds.

I gave him eagle feathers for his head dress.
They were truth singers
for making the mark of high courage.

I asked him to share with us
what he learned for our strength.

He told us:
    "I learned that there is no fear.
    All who say they are afraid,
    make the images they dance before their own eyes.

    Everything in the world is good,
    just for itself,
    just as it is.

    Everything is a friend,
    and is willing to help-care for us.

    Our fear is the only thing
    which keeps good from happening.

    When we let nature be our friend,
    life is full of hope."

GOODBYE, NADA, GOODBYE

by
Glen Scott, Partner, Friend, and Caretaker

Shortly before Nada's passing, I promised him I would do my best to make sure the books he had written, and especially "Face-of-the-Rising-Sun" would be published. This book is the fulfillment of my promise to him.

Some years ago, on our way over to Nada's mother's house in Roseburg Oregon, Nada and I walked over behind a small shed and as we were standing there, suddenly, a Red-tailed Hawk swooped down and screamed, perhaps 10 feet above our heads. "That's dad," Nada said. "He knows we're here, and is saying 'hello'. The Red-tailed Hawk is his Totem." We both stood there for several minutes, shaking, before heading to his mother's house. In the next days, Nada had a wonderful reunion with his Mother.

After a few months, Nada and I returned to Roseburg where Nada became a caregiver for his Mother. His father was buried on the property under a tree with three trunks. One day, Nada went to his father's grave to talk to him. While talking with his father, he became suddenly ill, and thought he was having a heart attack or stroke. His father told him. "You need to leave this property now. You are not safe."

Sometime in the night, Nada awakened me to say he was feeling bad and I should drive him to Eugene, Oregon, to the University Emergency Center. I had the car packed in about three minutes. He went to his mother's bedside and told her he needed to go to the hospital. She told him to go.

By the time we got to Eugene, Nada said he was feeling fine. We drove all the way back to Spokane. The following day, he went through a series of tests and the doctors found nothing. Further tests, however, revealed he had Parkinson's Disease.

From that time, I was honored to become Nada's caregiver until October 26, 2018.

In late October 2018, I looked out the back window and observed a magnificent Red-tailed Hawk sitting in a birdbath, and facing the house. I called Nada and helped him out of his chair to the window so he could observe the hawk.

He seemed surprised to see the hawk and then his face softened. "Hmmm," he said.

Later that day, he turned to me and said, "I want to die. I'm ready to go."

Sometime in the middle of the night, Nada awakened me and I helped him to the bathroom. I stepped into the kitchen to get a drink of water, and heard a crash. I rushed to the bathroom and saw him face down on the floor. I called the ambulance and the ambulance workers transported him to the emergency room. He was diagnosed with a broken collar bone. Shortly after his arrival he was given a shot to alleviate the pain, and lapsed into a coma but I took him home as he had requested. He never fully regained consciousness throughout the following week.

Each day, we saw a Red-tailed Hawk in the birdbath, facing our house.

On the morning of October 26, 2018, I noticed that Nada's breathing had changed. He was taking short, shallow breaths. As I called Hospice and asked for the on-call nurse I noticed the Red-tailed Hawk still in his usual post.

The nurse was there in a few minutes. She came into the bedroom and stood quietly for a moment. Then she turned to me and said softly, "It's okay. His breathing is telling us he is getting ready to pass away."

Afraid Nada could still hear us even though unconscious I said, "Can we step into the living room to talk?"

We sat down in the armchairs next to the burning fireplace. "I've never met you or Nada before, and this is my first visit to this house. When I came through the front door, I sensed the room was 'covered in spirit'."

"Thank you." Tears came to my eyes. I knew she was right.

At that moment, an alarm on her phone in the bedroom rang. We both jumped up and raced to the bedroom. I no longer felt Nada was in his body. I knew Nada had moved into Spirit.

Shortly after Nada passed, I looked out the window, and the Red-tailed Hawk was gone. It has never returned.

ABOUT NADA AS
WRITTEN BY HIM

I was born in an old log cabin in the Idaho Wilderness Area before it was declared wilderness.

Mother was part-Cherokee Indian and Dad was ¾'s a mix of Shoshone and Blackfoot Indian. Mother ran a pack-mule team. Dad worked for the Forest Service in the summer and a tribal trapper during the winter.

Because of the war, the U.S. Government moved us to Central Oregon where Dad worked in the timber and we lived in an old shack built of slab lumber, which we rescued from the tailings and irregular cuts from the mill.

When I was about five years old, I was with my parents in a forest watch tower, in the middle of a very stormy night. Suddenly, lightning struck both the tower and me, rendering me unconscious. However, somehow, I could feel the electric energy surge through my body. In retrospect, I believe etheric energy surged through me. Upon return to consciousness, I had lost my hearing. This condition continued for about one year before my hearing was restored.

For some time afterward, I was able to conduct acts of healing by touching people. It seemed to frighten my parents, so I learned to avoid openly to 'perform' healing.

Much of my knowledge of Native lore was learned from my father, and from an old Indian, one of the last Umpqua, who lived alone in a cabin nearby. The concept of "Face-of-the-Rising-Sun" has been with me throughout my life. The actual writing of this book didn't start until the early 1990s.

I've always had a natural communication and sense of oneness with other living things. When arranging plants in the garden, I often would ask where they would best like to be located. I communed with 300-year-old cedar trees. I asked for permission from my cat, Alpha, to pet her.

During the time I was writing *Face-of-the-Rising-Sun,* I spent many weekends with various members of the Lhaq'temish, the Lummi people, located on the Northwest Washington coast near Bellingham, Washington. The Lummi are fishers, hunters, gatherers, and harvesters of nature's abundance. They are the original inhabitants of Washington's northernmost coast and southern British Columbia.

On one occasion, I spent the night alone on an uninhabited island wholly contained within the boundaries of the Lummi Indian Reservation. I was able to reach the island on foot during low tide. Once there, when the tide came in, I spent the night, meditating, until low tide again.

At another time, with permission from the tribal elders, I spent the night in the Longhouse communing with the Ancestors over a fire, sharing the pages of *Face-of-the-Rising-Sun* with them. Emerging at daybreak, I was privileged to see three swans rise and fly upwards between me and the rising sun.

Once I began writing "Face-of-the-Rising-Sun", it just flowed through me, as though from memory.

ACKNOWLEGEMENTS

Special thanks to Dr. Jeri Lynn Miller for her
valuable feedback and encouragement.

Special thanks to Chaplain Paul Barber, who re-read the entire
manuscript to Nada and discussed edits prior to Nada's passing.

Special thanks to Josephie Dean Jackson and Anna Goodwin,
who shepherded "Face-of-the-Rising-Sun" through to publishing.

Special thanks to the Lummi Tribe for their hospitality to
Nada, Especially during the initial writing of this book.

Thanks to Robert Pope and Lawrence Konrad for their consistent
encouragement and support during the writing of this book.